Apollo

An Outer Space Economic Adventure

Barry Asmus

Introduction by
Apollo 13 Captain James A. Lovell

AMERIPRESS

Phoenix, Arizona

1-800-225-3864

Library of Congress Catalog Card Number: 96-83322

ISBN: 0-9640421-6-9

Cover design: Michael J. Slominski
Cover photographs courtesty of NASA

Published in the United States by
AMERIPRESS
3420 East Shea Boulevard, Suite 235
Phoenix, Arizona 85028

Manufactured in the United States of America

10 9 8 7 6 5 4 3 2

To teachers and parents who believe
that freedom and the market economy are ideas
worth passing on to the next generation.

Acknowledgments

To Pat Cox, a former student and friend who helped with an early draft of the book; to Mary Mitchell, a longtime friend and wonderful artist; and to James Lovell, a true American hero. I'm privileged to know him and honored by his thoughtful introduction to my book.

Introduction

It's been said that luck is where preparation meets opportunity. If that's so, I've been a lucky man indeed. America has provided me with more than my share of opportunities.

My career has taken me from a test pilot of the F4H "Phantom" Fighter, to serving as command module pilot and navigator on "Man's Maiden Voyage to the Moon," to being the executive vice president of Centel Corporation, one of the nation's largest communications companies.

I also have a lot to be thankful for. My most harrowing experience occurred during my fourth mission as spacecraft commander of the Apollo 13 flight in 1970. It was my second journey to the moon and a trip that unfolded like a science fiction movie. There we were, thousands of miles from the warmth of Mother Earth, engulfed in the emptiness of outer space when an oxygen tank exploded. With the failure of the service module's cryogenic oxygen system, we converted our lunar module, Aquarius, into an effective lifeboat. Fortunately the procedure worked, and we conserved both electrical power and water in sufficient supply to guarantee our survival in space and our return to Earth.

Perhaps it was my own space emergency that made Barry Asmus' book *Apollo* catch my attention.

Here is a story about space, economics, and charming little creatures that reintroduce me to Adam Smith's "invisible hand of the marketplace." Choice, enlightened self-interest, voluntary exchange, and free markets are some of the ideas woven into the entertaining story line. Every kid will relate to John and Elizabeth, brother and sister astronauts, who, when they stop teasing each other, are up to their ears in adventure. Their new friend Durkee is an amusing mixture of teddy bear warmth and Jeffersonian intellect— a modern-day Yoda who makes life understandable. He believes everyone needs an opportunity elevator to succeed.

As a pilot and an astronaut, I've seen the splendor of our magnificent planet. But as a businessman here on earth, I've watched the counterproductive economic policies and regulations that encumber entrepreneurship and production. It's quite a contrast with the economic system we discover on the planet called Mises. The wealth of a nation is its people. And productivity is best encouraged with proper incentives, economic freedom and private ownership capitalism. *Apollo* can be a dream or a reality. The choice is ours. . . .

CAPTAIN JAMES A. LOVELL
Chicago, Illinois

Contents

Chapter One

DECIDING ON TOMORROW

The hot sun felt good to John and Elizabeth Hart. It reminded them of their home in Hawaii. But their immediate surroundings were quite different. They were on the launch pad at Cape Canaveral in Florida. Even the nearby ocean reminded them of their home in Hawaii, except it was the Atlantic and not the Pacific that lapped the shore.

The jet ride their family had taken from Hawaii to Florida was short compared to the long journey they were about to take. Their parents were solar engineers who had been hired to set up solar energy collectors in space. They planned to pilot their sky-factory spaceship into orbit to beam energy from the sun's rays back to Earth. Their spaceship, Apollo, would be their home while they operated the sunstation. Their ship was named after the famous American space program that landed the first people on the moon.

Can you imagine leaving school for a whole year to go into space? John surely could. He could imagine leaving school to go anywhere! But Elizabeth knew it would be a great educational opportunity, and her parents agreed. They were hoping John would become excited about learning again. The young people knew they would miss their friends and activities, although they were sure the adventure of living in the sunstation would make up for all that. But as they stood admiring the shining metal hull of the Apollo's sleek body, they did not realize the kind of adventure they were about to experience.

"Well, kids," Mr. Hart announced, "this is the ship. Quite a piece of machinery, isn't it?"

"It's incredible, Dad!" John exclaimed.

"And beautiful," Elizabeth added. "Much more wonderful than the pictures we saw."

"Yes, it really is," their father agreed. "I only hope you'll feel that way when we get back."

"So do I," said Mrs. Hart as she gazed at the great booster rocket that would provide the thrust necessary to put the Apollo into orbit. Standing in its shadow, she brought out a clipboard.

"We should make a list of special things to take. Once we boost into orbit, there won't be any stores, and home delivery would be much too expensive. Where should we start?"

"Let's start with a television," John suggested. "After a year without television we wouldn't even know what was happening on Earth."

"That's true," Mrs. Hart admitted, "but televisions are built into the Apollo. Lots of things we will want are already part of the ship, so we won't have to put them on our list. Can you think of anything else we might need in space?"

They paused to think about the problem. Elizabeth came up with the first suggestion. "How about food? We'll need food."

John grinned. "I'll certainly go along with that. But I know something we'll need even more than food: water!"

"True enough, son," Mr. Hart agreed, "especially since we'll be growing some of our own food in space. We'll need lots of water for the hydroponic gardens and the recycling processes. But there's something we need even more than water."

The young people stared at each other as they thought.

Suddenly Elizabeth's eyes lit up. "Air! We'll have to take oxygen with us!"

"That's right, Elizabeth," Mrs. Hart said, "and there are other things we need to decide on, too. As a matter of fact, many have been left up to us. We can choose special food, or music, or video recordings— any number of things."

The notion that they could choose the food they would eat for the next year set their minds in motion.

"Pizza!" John blurted.

Elizabeth disagreed. "We don't need pizza."

"Why not?" John looked a little crushed. "We have to eat something. I'll bet those dieticians have planned nothing for us but broccoli, cauliflower, and lima beans. Yuck!"

"But those would be good for you, John," Elizabeth explained. "Besides, we don't need anything as fancy as pizza. We need vegetables and bread, some protein, and milk products like cheese, and—"

John interrupted. "You can get all those things on

one good pizza!"

Elizabeth thought for a moment, then nodded. "Well, what do we really need then?"

Mr. Hart answered, "That's hard to say. We could simplify our needs to the point that we just take food pills, but that wouldn't be much fun. When people say they need something, they can mean all sorts of different things."

Elizabeth said, "Maybe we really mean *want* when we say *need.*"

"There's more to all this than meets the eye," John decided. To John, wants and needs were always the same.

The family started toward the control room from which the technicians and engineers on Earth would guide their ship into space. It contained many instruments that would send a constant flow of information to their spaceship. The family wandered around with one of the engineers who showed them the rows of computer boards used in the launch process and the giant television screen that would monitor it. Mr. and Mrs. Hart were familiar with the mechanics and procedures of space flight. Their children, however, were not, so they stopped talking and just gazed at the room full of gadgets. It looked like the inside of a giant 747 cockpit. John could imagine all this equipment powering two huge speaker systems.

Back outside, they squinted with the sudden change in light.

Mr. Hart told the engineer, "After the kids buy some things this afternoon, we should be ready for tomorrow morning's takeoff."

4

The engineer looked down at the two excited astro-kids. "What are you going to buy?"

"It boggles the mind!" John said with a faraway look.

The engineer grinned. "I know where you could spend a little money."

"Where?" John asked.

"On a haircut," was the reply. "We're not getting a good fit with your helmet. The manufacturer designed them for test pilots with crewcuts."

"Do I have to, Dad? What about Elizabeth? Her hair is longer than mine."

"He's just kidding, son. But you might trim it a little. We are going to be gone for a year, you know. It'll be plenty long when we get back. Anyway, don't buy anything too bulky. We have only so much room. After we assemble the solar panels, we'll have plenty of space, but until then things will be a little cramped."

"That's right," Mrs. Hart continued the explanation. "The panels will form a very large field of energy collectors. They're yellow, so the whole thing will look like a giant sunflower when it's put together. Right now the panels take up most of the space in the Apollo, but as soon as we achieve orbit we'll move them outside and use the room for living space.

One of the nice things about space is that there's no weather, so the panels will be just as safe tethered outside the ship as they are inside. But because the cost of putting anything into orbit is very high, we have to make sure everything we take is worth taking."

"Let's take a puppy!" Elizabeth suggested. "We can

name him Sunspot."

Mrs. Hart smiled. "I'm afraid that would involve some difficulties. Can you imagine trying to house train a puppy in the total vacuum of space?"

Elizabeth thought for a minute. "I guess you're right. But it would be nice to have a pet along."

John agreed. "I think I'm going to miss the animals back home more than anything."

"What's this?" asked Mr. Hart. "Are we getting homesick before we've even left?"

"Oh, not really," Elizabeth answered. "But I will miss a lot of things, like my friends at school and our backyard."

"I know. But don't you think other things will make up for those?" Mrs. Hart asked.

"Yes," John finally admitted, "and I can hardly wait! Let's decide on what to take."

"I want a new robot," Elizabeth announced. "One you can program to talk another language. Mom, can we get a voice-modulated robot?"

"That's boring!" John protested. "Who wants to learn another language? Let's get a model remote controlled flying saucer. And we need compact discs, too."

"CD's!" Elizabeth said with a little scorn. "What do we need CD's for? We should take lots of paints. We'll have time to paint all kinds of things we can't even see on Earth."

"But I don't paint!" John objected.

"Well, I don't like your music!"

Mr. Hart had a suggestion. "Maybe we shouldn't decide for everyone. Maybe each of us should decide what we want for ourselves."

"Okay," said Elizabeth.

"Sure," John agreed. "If we decide for ourselves, we'll have the things we like."

"Now all we have to do is choose what's most important," Elizabeth concluded.

"And that's not always easy," their mother warned. "We have only a certain amount of money, so some things may be too expensive."

"How can we be fair then? What if the stuff I want costs a lot more than the things Elizabeth wants?" John questioned.

"There's an easy way to solve that problem. We'll give each of you the same amount of money, and you can do anything you want with it as long as we have room for whatever you buy. You can even pool your funds for something. Let's all go downtown, shop together for the things we'll all use, and then split up."

So the Harts spent the rest of the day shopping and doing the things they wanted to do one last time before leaving on their trip into space. Elizabeth went to a park and fed crackers to the ducks. John and his father went back to Cape Canaveral to watch a football game on television.

After their final medical check, it was finally time to settle down for their last night's sleep on Earth. Now only eight hours separated them from the big moment, and they anxiously awaited the morning sun.

Chapter Two

SCARCED TO DEATH

Remember what it's like to wake up and realize it's your birthday? That's just how Elizabeth felt when she woke up knowing they soon would be blasting off into outer space. The sun wasn't up yet, and neither was John. She had already tried to wake him twice.

Then Mr. Hart came in. "Earth to John. Earth to John. Are you going with us?"

"Go away, Houston," John retorted. "Wake me on the next orbit."

"Wrong, son! It's now! Let's go!"

As John began to wake up, he remembered how the Apollo had looked as it stood perched on its great booster that would push it into geosynchronous orbit. A geosynchronous orbit is one that is just the right height and speed to guarantee that a ship will remain over one spot on the Earth's surface. His daydream ended when he heard his dad's final "John!"

"This is it," John said to himself. "This is the day. Soon we'll be eating breakfast, putting on our space suits, and heading for the launch pad."

A knock on the front door announced a special breakfast prepared by the space dieticians, and soon the family was gathered around the dining table.

Elizabeth sat back in her chair. "Why are we the lucky ones? Why do we get a chance to live in space?"

Mrs. Hart answered. "Well, your father and I have worked very hard to learn how to pilot the Apollo and do what we've been hired for, and the company *is* paying us a great deal. Because they are pioneering the efforts of private firms in space technology, it won't be long before dozens of companies will be sending workers and their families into space."

"I never thought of the trip as a job," John said. "I'd do it for free! It's all so exciting and full of adventure!

"It's not all adventure, John," his mother continued. "We love what we do, and it is exciting, but people work for other reasons, too. We hope to make enough money from this job to be able to have some of the things we've always wanted but couldn't afford. We would like to buy a home, and we want to start saving so you and Elizabeth can go to college."

"So we're going into space to get all the things we want on Earth?" Elizabeth wrinkled her nose.

"Not really," Mr. Hart said. "If the clothes and food and cars people want just grew in gardens or just appeared on your doorstep, there would be no problem. But that's not the way it is."

John asked, "So when we get back to Earth, will we have everything we want?"

"What do you think? Will you ever reach a point where you won't want anything else?"

"No." said John. "I suppose not."

"That's right," his father agreed. "Most people want more than they have. Whenever there is not enough of something, we say it is *scarce*. For example, one of the things people will always want is energy. As oil and coal are used up, they cost more. And when prices rise, we either pay more for coal and oil or we start buying other products. That's one of the reasons the company hired us to explore solar energy possibilities."

"Well, I want another glass of orange juice," John announced. "How do I get that?"

"Try saying please," his mother recommended.

When the van met them outside the door, John and Elizabeth felt proud in their flight suits. Television cameras and reporters were waiting. It was unusual to see an entire family go into space, and lots of people were interested. The youngsters were happy as they rode to the launch area, although they were also a little nervous. As they drove up to the tower they heard a voice over the loudspeaker: "Lift-off in ninety minutes. Lift-off in ninety minutes. Final technical reports commence, please."

The engineer in charge met them with a laugh. "Your hair looks great, John. I'm sure your helmet will fit much better now."

The weather looked perfect for the launch. As the Harts rode the elevator up to board the Apollo, Elizabeth and John were more excited than ever. All their days of study and preparation were finally paying off.

John said, "If this is a dream, I hope I don't wake up!"

Forty minutes before the Apollo was to take flight, the family was strapped into the acceleration couches, made to fit each member perfectly. Mr. and Mrs. Hart were busy relaying dial and computer readouts to ground control. The minutes seemed to stretch into hours, but finally the three-minute count-down began. The young people wanted to giggle but quickly remembered to be quiet as their parents began the final procedures. Their hearts raced as they heard . . . "Ten, nine, eight, seven, six, five, four, three . . ." and the great rockets started to rumble. The Apollo shook, and they began to experience a heaviness as the ship gained speed. It felt like a carnival ride as the pressure intensified and they were pushed farther and farther into their seats. Fortunately they had spent long hours in a simulator to prepare for the forces of acceleration they were now undergoing. They had practiced in an object attached to a giant metal arm that spun around like a very fast merry-go-round. But within a few minutes the Apollo reached its maximum speed and acceleration force. The full burn (the firing of the main rocket) had lasted only five minutes, and as it ended, so did the pull on their bodies. They looked at each other, and John laughed. Elizabeth's hair was floating upward. They were in total weightlessness.

"We made it!" Elizabeth burst out.

"Just about," her father told her. "We'll enter final orbit a little later, but we're finished with the main rocket. It'll jettison any minute now."

At that moment a voice came from the radio: "Main rocket separation completed. Give us confirmation, Paul."

Mr. Hart answered, "Affirmative, ground control. How do things look from your angle?"

"Just fine, Apollo." The radio hissed with its usual static. "We're just finishing computations for the final course adjustment. By the way, Mary, if you'll look out starboard, you might see a comet. It's an uncharted one. Our experts say it must have spun off Halley's. It should circle the sun once and head away from the Earth. It'll be quite a sight from your position. We'd like you to take some readings on it."

"Thank you, flight center. I'll do that," Mrs. Hart answered. "We're ready to begin programming for course adjustment. Do you have the final data?"

"Not quite, Apollo. It seems the maneuvers will be more complicated than we expected." There was a pause in the transmission. "Did you notice anything during lift-off that would account for a course change?"

"Not really," she answered. "We did shake around a little more than I expected. That might have affected the guidance system."

"Thanks, Apollo. Please test the reset switch on the guidance system. We'll run some tests down here to see if we can find the problem. In the meantime, we'll proceed on the assumption that the atmospheric conditions were worse than calculated." There was another pause as ground control prepared for the data read-out. "Are you ready to begin read-out?"

Mrs. Hart gave the go-ahead, and they began to program the ship's computer for the adjustment. John and Elizabeth followed the conversation intently.

"Are you afraid, John?"

"Are you?"

"A little."

"I guess I am, too."

Mrs. Hart heard her children's voices and knew they were worried. "Hey now, let's not be upset. Remember, we've been trained for this kind of situation. We don't even know if anything is wrong yet. Let's just relax."

At that moment the small maneuvering rockets kicked in and there was a momentary surge of acceleration. Then everything returned to normal, and for the first time John and Elizabeth noticed the window in front of them. The stars looked brighter than they had ever seen them.

There was silence in the cabin as the minutes passed. The lights from the control board dimly lit the inside of the ship and flickered in various colors, giving a strange Christmas-like appearance. Although they were concerned with the current situation, the strange beauty of space was captivating. While their parents read displays and waited for news from flight center, neither John nor Elizabeth broke the silence. Both continued to stare into awesome space through a very narrow window.

Slowly, at one corner, a bit of green appeared. Both locked their eyes on the astonishing sight. Mrs. Hart happened to glance away from her console and saw the circle of colors drift into view. She touched her husband's shoulder, and they all watched as the Earth came into focus. The white pinpricks of stars paled beside the colorful beauty of their home planet as it made its grand promenade across the window.

Mr. Hart turned to his microphone. "Flight center, we have not stabilized. We are still in a slow roll. I'm going to turn off the microphone for a few minutes." He pushed a switch and turned to his children. "Do you know why we saw the Earth in the window?"

"Something's wrong, isn't it, Dad?"

"That's right. I would guess the stabilization unit has failed."

"What does that mean?" Elizabeth asked. "Are we in trouble?"

"No, honey," their father answered quietly, "but we may need help. The Apollo could land, because it has wings, but without a working guidance system, we can't know what would happen if we tried to maneuver with the rockets. Flight center will probably send another ship to bring us down and repair the Apollo."

"Oh no," John groaned. "Why don't they just tell us how to fix it? I thought we came here to get energy so we and the company could make some money."

"That's right," Mrs. Hart replied, "but some things are more important than energy and money."

"Like getting back to Earth safely," Mr. Hart interjected. "The people at flight center wouldn't have sent us if they weren't prepared to take care of emergencies like this. Our lives are the important thing now."

"That's true," Mrs. Hart agreed. "Our lives are the most important factors—much more important than money."

"After all," Mr. Hart added, "what good is money without your life?"

He turned to switch the microphone back on. "Flight center, this is Apollo. Have we come to the same conclusion?"

"Apollo, this is flight center. We are showing a malfunction in your gyroscopic stabilization unit."

"Our instruments confirm that. It may have broken during lift-off."

Flight center crackled back, "We're sorry to cut your trip short. It will probably be a couple of days before we can get someone up to give you a ride home. Is everything under control?"

"That's affirmative, flight center. We have enough food and water for a long time. We'll enjoy the vacation while we wait."

Flight center laughed. "You do that! Oh by the way, the last course correction pushed you closer to that comet. Let us know how close it will pass as soon as you can tell."

Mrs. Hart answered, "It's very difficult to see anything because of our slow rotation. Next time we come around we'll compute the comet's path and relay to you."

"Thanks a lot, Apollo. It's a real coincidence that you're up there in time to witness a brand new comet. It doesn't look as if it will come close enough to cause any harm, but do let us know its position."

"Okay, center, we should see it in just a few minutes."

The family began to talk about the accident and the delay it would cost them and their company. Mrs. Hart tried to cheer up Elizabeth, John, and even Mr. Hart as they all watched for the comet. When the spacecraft turned, a light came into view.

"It's bigger than I thought it would be," was Mr. Hart's first comment.

As the comet came closer his eyes grew wider. "Flight center, flight center. This thing looks like it's bearing down right on top of us!" His voice rose louder and louder. "Center! The comet fills the window and it's getting bigger!"

The youngsters were terrified. John paled and gripped the arms of his chair so hard his fingers turned white. Elizabeth squeezed her eyes shut as the brightness of the comet lit the inside of the cabin.

"It's going to hit us!" shouted Mr. Hart. "Fire the rockets! Any place is better than here!"

Mrs. Hart flipped two switches, but the Apollo just spun faster. As the comet overpowered their spacecraft, they gasped in terror and waited for the impact.

Mr. Hart repeated in shocked disbelief, "It's going to hit us!"

Chapter Three

SPACE WARP

They gripped their chairs and tensed for the shock, hoping that somehow they would make it through the impact. They waited and waited, but nothing happened.

After a few more moments of scary silence, Mr. Hart spoke. "I don't understand! It hit us! I saw it hit us!"

"It's a miracle!" Mrs. Hart exclaimed. "We went right through the comet, but we weren't even shaken! It was like . . . like . . . a space warp!"

John asked quietly, "Are we still alive?"

"I don't know for sure, but it feels like it," Elizabeth answered.

Mrs. Hart immediately tried the radio. "Flight center, flight center! We made it! It must have been some sort of energy field."

Mr. Hart's smile was the widest his children had ever seen. "Try again, honey. The radio may have been affected."

"Flight center. Do you read me? Please reply." She turned to her family. "It looks as though our radio was knocked out. We're safe, though. They can find us without a radio."

Mr. Hart was engrossed with his instruments. "It looks as if they may not need to rescue us. We seem to be losing altitude, and as soon as we re-enter the atmosphere, we'll be able to maneuver the Apollo to a safe landing. We should even stop spinning, since this ship was designed to fly like an airplane."

As Mrs. Hart got up from her acceleration couch to investigate the damage to the stabilization unit, Mr. Hart continued his attempt to contact Cape Canaveral on the radio. Reluctantly John and Elizabeth unbuckled their safety straps. Because of their weightless state they were able to move effortlessly toward the large window that wrapped around the front of the cabin. They stared at the stars as the ship spun slowly, giving them a complete view of the heavens.

Elizabeth squinted, thought, then began to look a little puzzled. "Somehow the stars look different."

"I know! I was just thinking the same. I wonder why?"

The large circle of the planet became visible again. They just stared. Elizabeth's brow wrinkled, and John pulled himself toward the window as if getting a few inches closer would make a difference in his view.

"I know why the stars look different!" he exclaimed. "They are different! That's not the Earth! I know the Earth when I see it, and that's not it!"

Mrs. Hart was just pulling herself into the room through a door in the back of the Apollo. She had the broken part of the stabilization unit in her hand. Elizabeth turned, pushed off the window, and grabbed her mother's arm.

"You've got to look, Mom! You've got to look where the Earth should be!"

Her mother frowned. "What do you mean, where the Earth should be?"

"You've just got to see."

By then Mr. Hart, too, was staring intently at the strange planet floating in space before them. "Honey, you really ought to take a look at this. Something's happened."

Mrs. Hart pulled herself along to the window, and they all studied the globe, searching for familiar shapes.

Mr. Hart wondered out loud, "It just doesn't fit. I don't understand."

"The comet, or whatever that thing was, obviously did something terrible." Mrs. Hart suggested. "The electrical circuitry was affected when we passed through it. Maybe the comet caused some kind of . . . change."

"Good grief." Mr. Hart pulled himself to his chair, buckled in, and stroked his chin as his children waited for his words. "You're right. It must have been the comet. It must have made some sort of a doorway or warp in space between this place and our world."

Mrs. Hart thought for a minute. "If it's a doorway, then we should be able to get out by going back through when the comet returns."

"If we can get to it," Mr. Hart added in a sober tone.

"And that's not very likely right now," Mrs. Hart agreed. She relaxed her grip around what she had brought from the back of the Apollo. Although she took her hand away, the glittering little pieces of glass floated in the air exactly where she left them.

"This is what's left of the spherical-silicate-antimagnetic-semiconductive gyroscopic stabilization unit bearings. Our stabilization unit is worthless. If we were a hundred yards from the comet, we couldn't get to it."

John asked, "What are spiritual-silly-antimajestic-semipreconductor bearings?"

Mr. Hart corrected him as he explained. "Spherical-silicate-antimagnetic-semiconductive gyroscopic stabilization-unit bearings are the glass ball bearings used in the gyroscope in our guidance system. Apparently they were broken during lift-off. Remember how shaky it was?"

Mrs. Hart reached out and took the pieces from the air. "They shouldn't have broken. They were made to withstand that kind of pressure. They must have been defective. But there is nothing we can do about it now."

"But what are they?" John asked.

"Well, basically, they are glass balls," his mother told him. "In other words . . . marbles."

"Marbles!" John and Elizabeth exclaimed together.

"Marbles," their father assured them.

"But marbles are so cheap," John said. "I must have a thousand of them back home."

"That's right," Elizabeth agreed. "Marbles are cheap."

"Well," their father sighed, "right now I'd give everything I own for a few of those cheap marbles."

"Everything you own?!" John was amazed.

"But marbles aren't that valuable." Elizabeth was

puzzled. "They hardly cost anything."

"Wait a minute," Mrs. Hart said. "Marbles are very inexpensive, but they would be of tremendous value to us now. *Value and price* are two entirely different things. If we had just twelve little marbles, we could maneuver back through the comet."

"Instead," Mr. Hart explained, "we'll have to land on this unknown planet and then hope we can figure out a way to fix the guidance system. Fortunately, we brought extra fuel tanks and may be able to take off again. That is, if we can fix the stabilizer."

Elizabeth shook her head. "It's unbelievable. This great big ship, and all of us are helpless without a few marbles, . . . a few cheap little marbles."

"Think about it like this," her mother offered. "If you were dying of thirst in the desert, which would be more valuable: an expensive diamond, or a drink of water?"

"Oh!" Elizabeth said.

"Amazing!" John said quietly.

"What's amazing, John?" his mother asked.

"It's amazing that we're orbiting around a mystery planet and that our destiny hangs on a handful of marbles."

His father replied, "Well, we're not going to be orbiting much longer. We're starting our descent. Our instruments say we'll soon be entering the atmosphere. So everybody buckle up and prepare for landing."

As the Apollo skipped along the top of the planet's atmosphere, its hull began to glow with heat. When it entered the atmosphere and slowed down, the temperature inside rose, although not to the point of being dangerous. The ship descended in a steep glide with Mrs. Hart at the controls while Mr. Hart studied the planet to locate a landing area. He chose a large meadow and the big ship landed as smoothly as a butterfly. As it skidded to a stop, Mr. and Mrs. Hart began to test the atmosphere. Their children, who had been speechless, finally started to talk.

"How exciting," Elizabeth chattered. "What do you think it's like outside?"

"How do I know?" John answered. "I just hope we won't have to wear our full space suits."

Mr. Hart was working with the computerized instruments. "I don't think we will. As far as I can tell, the atmosphere is almost identical to the Earth's. I don't understand what happened when we passed through the comet, but this planet appears to be very similar to ours. Even its size and gravity pull are similar, and yet our own scientists don't know it exists."

After reading the instruments and discussing options, the Harts concluded that their only chance to get back to Earth was to go outside and find a way to repair the Apollo.

Mrs. Hart warned, "Stick close to your dad and me. We didn't count on landing on a strange planet, and there's no telling what might live here."

"All I can see from the window is lots of plant life," Mr. Hart commented.

So the family prepared to explore the area. The youngsters were frightened, and so were their parents, though they tried not to show it. Cautiously, they opened the exit hatch and lowered the ramp. They peered out and looked carefully around as they walked down and stepped to the ground.

Elizabeth summoned up all her courage. "Well, we couldn't have picked a prettier place to be stranded. I wonder if anyone lives here."

John added, "Yeah, and I wonder what they eat!"

"Well, *we* might live here," Mr. Hart stated, "if we can't get some spherical-silicate-antimagnetic-semiconductive gyroscopic stabilization-unit bearings."

"Com'on Dad, you mean marbles," John corrected him.

"No matter what you call them, our guidance system won't work without them."

"I hope," Mrs. Hart added, "there is some sort of civilization here that will help us."

At that very moment the planet's inhabitants were on their way to greet them. The Apollo had come onto the scene with a great sonic boom and was visible for miles. Little blue and purple heads were making their way closer and closer.

At the same time, the Hart family noticed a path leading into the forest that surrounded the meadow. They walked carefully down the path, observing the many different types of plants and flowers. The sky was purplish-blue, and the sights and smells were like nothing they had experienced before. They hardly noticed the activity in a field ahead of them until they were practically on top of it.

Elizabeth was first to look up through the filmy leaves. Hovering above the field were two creatures that seemed to be some wonderful kind of bird. The family crouched down immediately so they would not be seen. The flying creatures floated like helium balloons, and though they had wings that waved gently, they looked like five-pointed golden stars as they shimmered in the sunlight, seeming to glow from inside.

The Harts were so entranced they almost missed what was happening below the bird creatures. A number of small human-like beings about the size of a ten-year-old child and covered with short woolly fur had gathered. The family couldn't help staring at the little folks with hairy coats of blue and purple.

"What are they?" Elizabeth asked.

"Don't ask me," John said. "I'm new here, too. They look like furry kids—furkids."

"That's pretty good, John," Elizabeth said.

"It's good enough for now, anyway," Mrs. Hart added. "I think the flying creatures look like . . . starbirds."

As the family watched, they began to understand what was going on. The starbirds floated down to the furkids and handed them the objects they were carrying in their beaks. In return, the furkids gave something to the starbirds before they floated away.

Mr. Hart noticed more starbirds coming toward the field. "Look over there. It looks like the starbirds are picking something off those spiky-looking trees. Then they fly back to the furkids." As the starbirds flew, the Harts got a better view of the objects they were carrying.

John was first to speculate. "I think they're carrying food. That thing looks like a giant raspberry. Here comes another one carrying a strawberry as big as a basketball. I'd sure like to try one of those berries."

"Can you tell what the furkids are giving the starbirds?" Mrs. Hart asked. "They look like little bottles. Yes, I think that's it."

Just then a starbird took a bottle, cradled it in its wing, and tipped it up to its beak.

Mrs. Hart said, "Apparently that's some sort of food, too. It looks like they're trading food."

"Terrific!" John, almost shouted. "We're saved. Somebody must be telling them what to do. All we have to do is find out who that is and ask for help. You know, like in science fiction. All you do is say, 'Take me to your leader,' and then ask for everything you need!"

Elizabeth was beginning to become excited, too. "That's right! All we have to do is find out who's in charge here."

Just then a little burst of giggles came from behind some bushes.

"Did you hear that?" Mr. Hart asked.

"I heard it," Elizabeth whispered. "But what was it?"

"Probably nothing," Mr. Hart assured them, not quite believing his own words. Attempting to distract the children, he asked, "Are you sure one person is telling everyone else what to do?"

"Why not?" John asked.

"Well, think about it." Mrs. Hart attempted to calm the children. "The furkids must want the fruit that grows on top of those tall, spiny trees. The trees are spread out all over the forest. Wouldn't it make sense for the starbirds to gather those big fruits? The birds don't have to walk through the forest to find the trees, and they don't have to climb them to see if they have fruit. They just see it, pick it, and bring it back."

"And the furkids are giving the starbirds some sort of liquid in a bottle," continued Mr. Hart. "How else would creatures without fingers handle liquid?"

"I see what you mean," John said, "but I still think someone in charge is telling them what to do."

"You mean you don't think they could figure it out by themselves?" Mrs. Hart asked.

"It's just common sense," Elizabeth said with a smug little smile.

"This trading probably takes place because it results in everyone being better off. Perhaps no one is in charge." Mrs. Hart had just finished speaking when they heard a thump behind them, followed by a burst of laughter. They turned to see that a tiny blue creature had fallen out of the tree where it had been spying on them. It hopped up and ran into a bush amid hidden laughter.

"Now, that's something," John said with wide eyes.

But the noise from the furkid children attracted the attention of the adult furkids the Hart family had been observing. They all turned to face the Harts, and even the starbirds wanted to see what the disturbance was. The Harts nervously faced the group.

"They seem friendly enough," Mr. Hart commented.

"A little shy, though," John added.

"Just cautious," Mrs. Hart decided, "and we should be, too."

The group in the field made its way toward the

Harts, and the Harts, trying to be brave, started toward them. The youthful furkids followed them out of
the forest.

"Well," Mr. Hart ventured, "shall we introduce ourselves?"

Chapter Four

TOOL TALK

From a distance the furkids had looked very strange, but as the Harts came closer they were over-whelmed by the creatures' appearance. Although they were beautifully colored, most amazing were the two antennae that protruded a hand's length from each of their heads. They looked like black plastic tubes, each topped with a little ball. They were not stiff but seemed to bend and twist toward whomever they were communicating with at the time. All the antennae were now bent toward the Harts. Except for the slight move-ment of their wings, all the starbirds hung motionless a few yards apart. At such close range, the family could see that the starbirds had large, warm eyes, and there seemed no doubt that they were intelligent. The creatures were just as amazed as the humans, and it was quite a while before the silence was bro-ken. Finally one blue furkid, apparently a female, stepped forward and made a sound as if clearing her throat.

She began, "Ourdas redobzou, kidb. Redilub sratnus?"

Stunned, Mrs. Hart asked, "What?"

The furkid caught the meaning of the question and repeated, "Ourdas redobzou, kidb. Redilub sratnus?"

Mrs. Hart told her husband, "I don't think we're going to be able to talk with these folks. What should we do?"

Then Mr. Hart tried. "I'm afraid I don't speak your language, friends. Anybody here speak English?"

The starbirds made no sound, and the furkids remained quiet, though their antennae stretched forward even more.

"Just kidding. I sure wish I could talk to you." Even though they didn't answer, Mr. Hart had the impression that they understood his joke. It gave him a shiver.

One furkid turned to the others and said, "Bradus reseada dar, mrantus," which probably meant something like, "They obviously don't speak our language. I wonder where they're from?"

One of the starbirds answered the furkids question in a low whistling melody. A discussion followed among the different creatures, obviously concerning what the strange visitors were doing, where they came from, and what they should do about it. As they were communicating among themselves, Mr. Hart noticed the bottle that hung around a nearby starbird's neck by a delicate chain.

"Look at that bottle," he said. "Whoever made that is very skilled."

"It's a work of art," Mrs. Hart agreed. "Do you know what that bottle means?"

Mr. Hart took his wife's hand. "It means that they may be able to manufacture glass bearings for the guidance system."

"Oh boy, we're saved!" John erupted. "Gee, I hope we have time to get to know these people before we leave."

"John, these aren't people. They're alien life-forms," Elizabeth instructed.

"They're not aliens! We are!" John snapped. "Besides, they seem as intelligent as some of *your* friends."

All Mrs. Hart had to say was "John!"

"We're not home yet, John," his father lectured. "Just because they may be able to make glass marbles doesn't mean we can take off. If we don't repair the ship before that comet comes back, we may have our whole lives to get to know them."

"Let's find out who's in charge here," Elizabeth suggested.

"We have just one little problem," Mrs. Hart pointed out. "We don't speak their language, or languages. We need to be able to communicate with them."

"That's right," Mr. Hart agreed. "They may have exactly the parts we need right over the next hill, but without their help, we'll never know."

The furkids and starbirds stopped their discussion and turned to face the Harts. One small blue furkid, a young man, stepped forward. He stuck his chest out, pointed at it with his thumb, and said, "Durkee."

Mrs. Hart asked in a questioning tone, "Durkee?"

The little blue creature smiled and repeated the gesture.

Elizabeth whispered, "Look, he has one less finger than we have."

Mr. Hart stepped forward, touched his chest, and said, "Paul."

Durkee tried to repeat the word: "Paaal."

The children both laughed, then stopped suddenly. They were afraid they might have hurt the little fellow's feelings. Although he didn't seem offended, he was startled by the sound of laughter. His eyes widened, but his smile showed he was not afraid. Then the rest of the furkids began to laugh, and the family couldn't help laughing with them. Even the starbirds were affected. They began to whistle a cheerful tune, turning cartwheels in the air. As the Harts' fear faded, and when everyone had quieted down, Durkee went to John and took his hand. The other furkids grabbed the hands of the other Harts, motioning them to come.

"Wait a minute," Mr. Hart gently protested. The sun was beginning to sink below the horizon. "It's getting dark, and we really ought to get back to our ship for the night."

The furkids seemed to understand exactly what Mr. Hart said and instantly stopped tugging at the family. Once again the Harts wondered how the creatures understood their intentions without understanding their language. Then all the furkids except Durkee started to make their way home, calling out, "Mashlahh, mashlahh."

The family took the cue perfectly and called back, "Mashlahh, mashlahh," which started the furkids clapping and laughing again as they walked away.

Mrs. Hart looked down at Durkee. "Evidently we have a guide here."

"And a guest," John added.

Mrs. Hart speculated, "My guess is that he is our translator. We can either teach him English or learn his language."

"I vote for his learning ours," John concluded.

Durkee, in fact, was their translator. All furkids do some communicating without speech because of the function of their antennae, but Durkee was especially good at this. The family was about to learn that for themselves.

They started back to the Apollo, and although the children were tired from the day's excitement, they were enthusiastic about having Durkee spend the night. Mr. and Mrs. Hart thought about the bottles and hoped they would lead them back to Earth. Learning to communicate with Durkee was a game to the kids, but it was serious business for Mr. and Mrs. Hart. Without his help, the situation seemed hopeless. They planned to use the Apollo's computers to determine how long it would be before the comet would circle the sun and be gone forever. They were afraid they didn't have very much time at all.

Their first night on the planet was a busy one. Mr. and Mrs. Hart estimated the comet would return in about three weeks; they would make precise computations later. At the same time, John and Elizabeth tried to teach Durkee English. He learned at an extraordinary rate. Before the Harts went to sleep Durkee was counting, calling everyone by name, and identifying various parts of the body. That was especially fun, because some of Durkee's parts were not like human parts at all. He gazed with great interest at ears, since he had none, and the children were equally interested in his antennae.

While the Harts slept, Durkee made a quick inspection of the computers and monitors. He came across the television and video equipment, figured out how it worked, and was soon studying the entertainment tapes the Harts had brought with them. Playing them on fast forward, the actors' voices sounded like a choir of chipmunks. Durkee's antennae went wild as he tried to digest all the sounds and actions of the programs. His favorites were the space movies, and he fell asleep dreaming he was a Jedi knight, determined to save a lovely princess on a planet far, far away. In the background of the dream Hans Solo was saying to Chewbacca, "Go ahead, laugh it up, Fuzzball!" Durkee was a fast learner indeed.

The next morning started just like any other, with breakfast. The meal consisted of scrambled eggs, toast, and peaches; prepared Earth-style. The children dug in, but Durkee was a bit more cautious. He sniffed carefully at the little plastic containers and tried the eggs first. Seemingly unfamiliar with silverware, he took some eggs in his hand and nibbled them slowly. He put them down and gave Mrs. Hart a polite look, his way of apologizing for not being a good guest. Next he picked up some toast, took a tiny bite, stared at the ceiling as he chewed, and put the toast down. He picked up a peach slice, sniffed it, held it up to the light, and finally nibbled it. He suddenly sat back and stared at the peaches. He took a larger bite and chewed more confidently. Then, as if a light had gone off in his brain, he quickly devoured the remaining peaches.

"We know he likes peaches, anyway," Mr. Hart murmured.

With a flourish, Durkee drank down the last of the peach juice. Mrs. Hart went to the storeroom to get another container, and he finished this second helping of peaches with obvious pleasure just as the family was ready to leave the Apollo.

"Where are we going?" Elizabeth asked.

"We were hoping Durkee had some place in mind." Mrs. Hart told her.

"Let's see if he takes us to his leader." Elizabeth ventured.

Durkee did indeed have a place in mind. He started down the ship's ramp, and the adventurous band of explorers was off. They followed their little guide through growth so dense the path looked more like a jungle trail. The forest seemed to close in around them, and the unfamiliar sights and sounds made the family doubt whether they were in friendly territory.

"I wonder, do they have dangerous animals here?" Elizabeth asked. "You know, like lions and tigers and bears."

"Come on," John laughed uneasily "Durkee doesn't seem to be worried, so I don't think I will be either."

"Well, excuse me!" Elizabeth exclaimed. "I didn't know you were so brave."

The path ended in a clearing, and just as they came into the sunlight, a bright pink football-shaped object came flying toward them, hit the ground, and rolled to Elizabeth's feet. Then, just as suddenly, two very young furkids came tumbling after it. One grabbed it and was tackled by the other. They laughed and wrestled, and when the object flew into the air again, they went after it.

The Harts were wondering what sort of game the little furkids were playing when Durkee said, "Foot."

"Foot?" they asked in curious unison.

"Foot," Durkee affirmed.

John pointed to his extended foot. "This is foot."

"Oh." Durkee searched his wordbank "Not foot. Maybe, food?" He gestured toward his mouth as if eating.

The family continued to watch the furkids throwing the pink football food around until one of them took it to a rock and began to pound it again and again, but with no noticeable effect. Then the other furkid threw the thing straight up in the air as hard as he could. As it came down it hit the same rock, and broke in half. The furkids divided it; then they took small seed-like things out of it and popped them into their mouths.

Durkee had been busy while the family watched the little furkids. Poking about through the vegetation, he gave a happy shout when he found what he was looking for. The children ran to his side and their parents followed, surprised to see another pink football growing on a vine. Durkee called the young furkids, who stopped eating long enough to come and listen. They discussed something, and Durkee took a few discs from the cape he was wearing. He gave them to the furkids, plucked the pink football, and handed it to Mrs. Hart.

"Food," he said, confidently this time.

"It's hard as a rock," Mrs. Hart said as she handed it to Mr. Hart.

He tossed it from one hand to the other. "Now I know why those kids were hitting it so hard." He handed it to John and Elizabeth, who examined it closely.

Durkee said, "Come now," and started down the path.

"He's learning fast, isn't he?" Mrs. Hart looked puzzled. "As a matter of fact, I don't remember anyone using any of those words around him. Well, let's follow."

John smiled. "I hope he learns even faster, so we can ask him when we get to eat."

Elizabeth responded, "I think its more important, John, if he takes us to his leader."

As they followed Durkee up a steep path, they noticed a large mushroom-shaped object at the top of the hill. Durkee walked up to it, knocked on a circular door, and began visiting with a pig-tailed furkid. She ducked back into her house, to emerge a minute later with a shiny metal apparatus. Slightly larger than the pink football plant, it was hollow and had a handle on top. Durkee put the plant into the machine and turned the handle slowly. The football-shaped plant began to creak with stress, like a huge nut about to break. Then there was a loud crack and the plant split down the middle. Durkee jumped around gleefully and handed half the plant to the Harts.

John took one of the seeds and bit into it. "Chocolate!" he exclaimed.

"And cherry!" Elizabeth squealed. "This is a chocolate-cherry plant!"

The family loved the treat. Rubbing his full tummy,

Durkee seemed to enjoy watching them eat his food as much as they had enjoyed watching him eat theirs.

When John finished, he studied the chocolate-cherry-plant-cracker more closely. "This is a neat gadget, Durkee," he said finally. "We don't have any tools quite like it on our planet."

"A tool?" Elizabeth asked. "Why would you call that funny looking contraption a tool? It just looks like a nut-cracker to me."

John tried to explain. "Isn't a tool something you use to make things a whole lot easier? With this little machine, Durkee managed to fix us lunch in a few seconds. The way those two kids in the field went about it, it could've taken us all day to eat."

"I wonder what they did before they had these crackers?" his sister asked.

"I'll bet," observed Mrs. Hart, "they worked a lot harder and ate a lot less chocolate-cherry plant."

All the talk about tools suddenly reminded Mr. Hart of their plight. "Our spaceship is a tool. As a matter of fact, our guidance system is a tool . . . or was a tool."

"Those are tools?" Elizabeth asked turning to her father. "Then if we can't fix the old ones, all we have to do is figure out how to make new ones right?"

"That's usually a lot easier said than done," replied Mr. Hart. "In order to build a tool or machine of any kind, you have to save things instead of using them." He looked at their expressions and explained. "If a farmer wants a tractor or a scientist wants a computer, they have to save enough money to buy them. Hawaiians, in the old days, had to fish almost all the time just to have enough to eat. But by storing dried fish, they were able to use the time to make new nets to catch even more fish."

"I get it. Our spaceship is like a net." John sounded thoughtful.

"You're right," Mrs. Hart assured him. "If people used everything they made, nothing extra would be left over to build new things like our spaceship. Those extras, or tools, are what make our life better and easier."

"I'm glad John wasn't one of the old Hawaiians. He wouldn't have stopped eating long enough to make a net," Elizabeth chirped.

"I see what you mean now," John said as if he hadn't even heard his sister. "Fishing nets and our spaceship are just two of the things that make us different from animals. We have the ability to think and choose. But what does that have to do with marbles?"

Mr. Hart's forehead wrinkled. "Well, I'm not sure yet. There's only one way to find out, though. We'll just have to keep going and hope we find a way to get the tools we need to fix the Apollo."

Chapter Five

NO MONEY, NO MARKET

The chocolate-cherry plant made a fine early lunch, and they felt ready to continue their tour of the strange planet.

"Go now!" Durkee said, and the family followed. Although his legs were shortest, he made up for that by trotting while the others walked normally.

Unfortunately, the Harts had had no chance to examine the new planet before they landed and were not sure how the furkids and starbirds lived. The first dwelling they had seen was the mushroom-shaped one where they borrowed the plant-cracker. It turned out to be very close to Durkee's village. As they came closer they heard the beep-beep of a horn and turned just in time to see a hovercraft pass quickly. Driven by two furkids, it skimmed over the ground just like Earth hovercrafts that ride on a cushion of air.

"Well, how about that," Mr. Hart exclaimed. "I was wondering how advanced their technology is. If they can build hovercraft, they may be as advanced as we are."

John was glad to hear that. Though he was having a good time exploring the new planet, he knew he didn't want to spend the rest of his life away from his friends and the things he loved on Earth.

After a moment's thought, Mr. Hart said, "I think hovercraft are better than vehicles with wheels. They need only a smooth path free of big rocks or trees, rather than a paved road. And the electric powered hovercraft can even keep the grass down."

As they walked, Elizabeth, looking around for new mysteries, noticed a flurry of activity. Durkee ran ahead, but turned back to shout, "Move buns faster." The Harts stopped in their tracks, wondering where he had picked up such slang. Durkee sensed he had made an error in his choice of words and, embarrassed, corrected them. "Come. See. Please."

Giggling to themselves, the Harts quickly reached an area where they found all sorts of fascinating things. Furkids and starbirds were inside tents, talking, laughing, or just sitting as their children scurried about. On closer examination, they noticed many starbirds carrying the same giant fruit they had seen earlier. Some furkids were carrying flowers, or other objects so foreign the Harts had no idea what they were.

"What's going on?" John asked.

"Looks like one of your rollerblade competitions," Elizabeth replied sharply.

Durkee understood the questions but seemed to have trouble finding the words to answer. Not wanting to embarrass himself again, with much quivering of antennae he finally said, "They give . . . and take."

"Give and take?" John was puzzled, so he began to watch.

Two interested furkids approached Durkee to ask

questions. And though they weren't sure, the Harts thought one of them was snapping their picture.

Most of the activity appeared to involve different objects or products. The children noticed that everyone carrying chocolate-cherry plants went to one area. Several furkids would look at the plants and start a discussion. When they saw one furkid give another a few disc coins for his plant, Elizabeth knew what was going on.

"I get it?" she exclaimed. "They're not giving and taking, they're buying and selling. This must be a market or a mall."

John was puzzled, "Can you have a market without any buildings or cash registers?"

Mrs. Hart explained. "Of course you can, John. Markets aren't just buildings. Whenever someone buys, sells, or trades something, it is called a market. At school, when you trade a peanut butter and jelly sandwich for a tuna salad sandwich, you've created a market. Lots of markets take place over the telephone, but the telephone isn't the market. A market is really the action that takes place when trading is going on."

"Remember earlier, when Durkee borrowed the tool to crack the plant?" Mr. Hart continued the explanation. "Did you notice that Durkee gave his friend some of the seeds?"

"Yes, I did," Elizabeth answered, "but I thought he was just being nice."

Her father went on, "He was being nice. It's also nice to pay people for their help. Just because you don't do something for free doesn't mean you are not kind. When you give something in return for a favor, then that, too, is a market."

The family noticed a number of furkids who were particularly interested in one starbird's fruit that was different from the others. It looked like a huge blue diamond with a stem. The crystal-like walls of the skin were transparent, and the fruit was filled with a bluish liquid. Everyone seemed eager to buy it. When one furkid held up three fingers, another held up four, and this continued until one held up all eight fingers. As the starbird acknowledged this bid with a low whistle, the furkid counted out eight discs and was handed the fruit.

"It looks as if they're selling their fruit to whoever will pay the most money," John observed.

Durkee agreed with John's conclusions. "Very good. Those who pay most want it most."

The family was amazed at Durkee's correct use of English, and his bluntness. They were beginning to realize that he was somehow reading their minds to find the appropriate words.

Mr. Hart asked, "Can you think of a better way to decide who should get what?"

"But, Dad, it just doesn't seem fair," Elizabeth said.

"Why not?" Mrs. Hart agreed with her husband. "No one forces them to buy or sell. Those who buy would rather have the fruit than the money and those who sell would rather have the money than the fruit. It works out just right. Everyone's happy."

"But why do they use money instead of just trading their goods?" asked Elizabeth.

Mrs. Hart was about to explain when she was interrupted by the cry of a furkid who flew through the air, did somersaults, and landed on his feet to take a bow. His entrance was followed by a troupe of musicians and acrobats. Some sang and played violin-like instruments; some danced and performed stunts for the gathering audience; another group flipped one another high into the air, did amazing twists and turns, and always landed perfectly on their feet. As the show ended, two acrobats held a musician's cloak between them and wandered through the audience. The crowd voiced their approval and thanks by flipping coins into the cloak. When they had collected as much as they could, the troupe touched hands to antennae, did full spins, and ran off to perform in another area of the market.

"Whew!" John gasped as if he had been an acrobat himself. "That was some performance. If this is a market, I love it. Did you see all the money?"

Durkee seemed very interested in the conversation. His antennae was quivering again. Removing a pouch that had been hanging on a tiny chain around his waist, he emptied its contents into his hand for the family to see.

"Blahfap," he stated. The Harts stared with puzzled expressions. "Oops," Durkee said, then blurted out, "Money," so the family could understand.

The Harts nodded and looked at the little discs in his hand. Some were metal and others were little dishes of plastic. There were round coins and square coins; some were five-or six-sided; but most had pictures and writing.

"No money, no market," Durkee said as he gestured toward the activity going on about them.

Mr. and Mrs. Hart again nodded in agreement. As Durkee watched them, he tried nodding. It was funny to see the little blue furkid mimic the Harts.

"I still don't get it," John admitted. "Why do you need money to have a market?"

Durkee understood, but he couldn't explain. With his limited English, many questions were difficult to answer.

Mrs. Hart came to his rescue. "Can you imagine what it would be like if we had to trade the things we made for the things we wanted? What if you wanted a . . . a comic book from someone who wanted a pair of rollerblades. You would have to hunt around until you found someone with the rollerblades, and then find out what he wanted in exchange for it."

"Sounds like a long process," John decided.

"Exactly," Mr. Hart said. "Without money, people would spend most of their time arranging trades instead of making the things other people want. Societies would probably stay underdeveloped if they did things that way."

Elizabeth was surprised. "I never thought about money that way before."

"Well, it's a good sign they have money here, because it means they have a specialized economy. My guess is that we have a better chance of getting home because they have a monetary system."

John, who had been only half listening as he watched the crowd, suddenly had a flash of inspiration. "Money!" he exclaimed. "It's the government that prints money and makes coins! Now we can find out who's in charge! Just find their government, and we're home free!"

There was a scowl on Durkee's face as he tried to understand John's enthusiastic outburst.

"What is guv-er-munt?" he finally asked.

"They're the guys who make the money and control the country!" John explained.

Durkee's right hand went up to stroke one of his antennae. He was thinking very hard.

"John's right, Durkee," Elizabeth confirmed. "Who's in charge here? Who *does* make the money?"

"Oh." Durkee seemed relieved by that question. "We make money. We all make money." And he looked around at everyone in the market.

"You made these?" Elizabeth pointed to the coins.

"No." He laughed. "Money is because we . . . believe."

"What does he mean?" John asked his parents.

"I can't help you," Mr. Hart admitted.

"What is money?" John asked Durkee.

Durkee's hand went to an antenna again. He took a long time to think about the answer. Finally he said, after so much thought it seemed to pain him, "Money is an . . . idea."

"Now I'm really confused," John said.

"So am I," Elizabeth added.

"Well, let's think about it," Mrs. Hart tried to help. "I think what Durkee is saying is really not all that mysterious. What if we had a million dollars right here? What good would it be? Or if we had it in the middle of the desert, or shipwrecked on an island?"

John simply scratched his head.

"You might be able to build a fire with it if you were cold," Elizabeth offered.

"And that's about all," Mr. Hart added. "Money has value only when everyone agreed it has value. For a society to work, everyone has to believe money can buy things."

The Harts stayed and talked at the market until it was very late. Durkee invited them to spend the night at his house, for which they were very grateful. Fortunately, all the homes along the path were lighted so they could see.

Elizabeth asked one last question. "Where does it all come from, though? Where does money start?"

Durkee answered, "It comes when new things are made."

Mr. Hart was quick to try to clarify Durkee's answer. "We don't really buy things with money—we buy things with other things. How can I say? Money is just a way to keep our wealth in small packages."

"That's right," Mrs. Hart added. "Money is a promise to others that you will give them real things for their money."

"But what happens when people print money without doing any work?" John asked.

"That's called counterfeiting," his father told him. "And it's stealing. It destroys the whole concept of money. You should print more money only when you can produce more things."

Just then an angry looking furkid marched toward them. Durkee sensed his approach and turned to greet him.

"Grabzo delostsus, doola!" the furkid shouted.

Durkee stepped back, looked at the Harts, then again at the furkid. They talked very fast. As Durkee explained, the look on the other furkid's face and the tone of his voice softened. Turning away from his friend, Durkee explained to the family.

"This is owner of field where spaceship landed," he began. "He did not know it was accident. He was very . . . not happy."

The owner of the field smiled meekly and said something else to Durkee, who translated. "He is not mad now. He wants to know when you will move spaceship from his field."

That took the Harts by complete surprise.

"What do you mean, move it?" Mrs. Hart asked disbelievingly. "A spaceship can't be moved."

"But it is his field," Durkee quietly explained. "Not yours."

Mrs. Hart closed her eyes. "That's all we need."

"And I thought they were all so friendly," John complained.

Durkee seemed to understand the Harts' concerns. He turned to the field owner to continue the conversation. The two argued. Durkee would say something, but his friend would turn away as if he could not believe what had just been said. The expression on Durkee's face was pained. Finally he turned back to the Harts.

"Will you let him take others through your ship for half the admission price?"

Mr. Hart was amazed. "Do you mean he will let us leave the ship there if we let him show it to others and keep half the money?"

Durkee's antennae twitched and his brow wrinkled from concentration. "Yes," he said simply.

"I thought we were in trouble," John said, "and suddenly we're making boo-coo bucks. All right! I think I like this place after all."

Mr. and Mrs. Hart whispered together. Then Mrs. Hart told Durkee, "We will give you half our money from the tours, if you will stay with us and help us find a place to live while we're here."

Durkee seemed delighted. He grinned. "Very good, very good."

The field owner and Durkee worked out the deal and ended by touching antennae. Then Durkee and the family were off again.

In a short time the Harts found themselves in Durkee's house. They were surprised to find he lived with his mother and father. After everyone was introduced, the family ate as much supper as they wanted and were shown to their rooms. John and Elizabeth fit into furkid beds, although Mr. and Mrs. Hart had to push two full-size beds together. As they ended the day with their customary family prayer, they were particularly thankful for a safe place to sleep.

Chapter Six

BANKING ON INTEREST

Elizabeth slowly opened her eyes and looked around the room. At first she was startled that she was not home in Hawaii. Then she began to think about all the interesting things she had learned in the short time they had been stranded on this violet skied planet. Although still somewhat apprehensive, she decided the best thing to do was to get up and get going.

At breakfast the Harts, Durkee, and his parents shared one of the giant fruits the starbirds had picked and finished their meal with nuts that tasted like almonds, coconuts, and french fries. Durkee offered juice, but it was so sour it made their lips pucker.

After breakfast Durkee held up his pouch and asked the children, "Are you still curious about money?"

"Who isn't?" both replied.

Mr. Hart answered, too. "Yes, Durkee. I think all of us are interested."

As Durkee was about to respond, there was a thump at the door. His father went to the door and brought back a magazine, which was, in fact, the furkids' newspaper. On the first page was a picture of the Harts and Durkee, taken the day before at the market. Another picture showed the Apollo in the field where it had landed. Across the top of the page were squiggles, obviously headlines. Durkee's parents seemed excited and began to read the story together.

Durkee told the Harts, "You are famous!"

To that Mrs. Hart said, "How do you know the *word famous, Durkee?*"

Durkee smiled. "I learn fast."

"I guess so," Mrs. Hart agreed, "especially since I know we've never used that word around you."

Durkee seemed anxious and tried to hurry the family outside to his hovercraft. They climbed aboard, he started the engines, and the skimmer raised off the ground and shot forward. Although they passed many factories that contained complex machinery, they decided to wait for a more opportune time to ask about glass ball bearings.

Durkee finally parked in front of a building with two sections. One section was a tower that rose high above their heads, and the other section stood on three legs. As they approached, they saw a starbird flying from a door at the very top of the tower. On the roof of the three-legged building was perched a giant disc that looked very much like the money Durkee had shown them.

"Sell money here," Durkee announced as he jumped out of his skimmer. The family joined him and they walked over to the elevator at the bottom of the tower. They rode to the top floor, where it opened onto an expansive reception area.

"Hey," John said, "this looks like a bank." He saw a furkid carrying a sack full of discs to a teller behind the counter.

"They buy money here, too," Durkee continued his explanation.

"What?!" John exclaimed. "This is crazy—buying and selling money. Is everyone on this planet a coin collector?"

"Collect?" Durkee was puzzled. "No, we just use them. We use money."

Mrs. Hart was smiling and finally started to chuckle. "You're right, John. This is a bank."

"Dad, what do they do here?" Elizabeth asked.

Mr. Hart answered, "Have you ever heard of interest on loans? That's how the bank makes money. Interest is the money you have to pay when you borrow money."

Durkee's antennae seemed to spin as he cried out, "That's right . . . *BORROW!* Pay to borrow money! Many furkids borrow money. My father borrowed money to build his factory. Many of my friends borrowed money to build their homes."

"I thought banks just protect money," John said.

"Oh, banks do much more than that," Mrs. Hart explained. "Why would banks pay people for the use of their money, if all they did was sit around with guns and protect it?"

"Never thought of that," was John's honest reply.

Durkee added, "This is a money market."

"A money market?" Elizabeth pondered.

"Remember when your father talked about saving and fish nets?" Mrs. Hart asked Elizabeth. "Well, instead of storing dried fish to feed his family, the fisherman could have borrowed fish from his neighbor while he was making his net. Now, don't you think the fisherman who loaned him the fish should be repaid, plus some? That extra he would be paid is called interest. This way, both fishermen would be better off, all because of the additional fish caught with the new net."

"I see," Elizabeth answered. "That seems fair."

"And had there been one, the fisherman could have gotten the same results by going to a bank for a loan," Mrs. Hart added. There was a moment of silence as the kids thought the whole thing over.

"Okay. It makes sense," John finally said. "If I were the fisherman who gave up some of my fish so the other guy could eat while he made a net, I would like to get something more in return, too."

Durkee rubbed an antenna. "What is fish?"

The Harts were speechless for a moment, then broke into laughter.

Elizabeth told him, "I'll try to explain later. But first let's finish our talk about interest."

"Oh," he beamed, "very interesting stuff."

With their laughter, the aliens had attracted even more attention than usual. When they settled down again, Mr. Hart continued to unravel the puzzle.

"Durkee's right. It is interesting. We have talked about how important tools are. Well, without investment we wouldn't have nearly as many of the nice things in life. All our houses, churches, cars, clothes, and books were produced because people were willing to save, invest, and work. Without savings, the Apollo never would have been built, and the things we all enjoy wouldn't exist. And without nets and tools, we'd all still be fishing and farming."

"Oh," John said. "Then money and savings provide for more than just fishing and farming."

"Yes," Durkee answered. "Investments like my parents thuralemm factory never would have been made without savings and money borrowed from banks."

"What's a thuralemm?" Elizabeth asked.

"Let's go see," Durkee replied.

"As long as thuralemm is something to eat," said John, "I'll go. If not, they'll have to wait. All this talk of fish has made me hungry."

"No, John, you'll have to be patient," his mother instructed, and gave him one of her looks.

They were soon standing outside a large square building with a picture of a violin on the front. They recognized the instrument as the one the entertainers in the marketplace had played. At one end of the building, a stack of wood was being unloaded from a very large hovertruck. Durkee's father came out to greet the family.

"My father says he is pleased you have come to see the thuralemm factory. He would like you to see as much as you want."

The Harts expressed their appreciation, and they all walked into the building. There was activity everywhere. At the end of the building where the lumber was being unloaded, furkids were placing it near a saw so it could be cut into different shapes. Some shapes were for the thuralemm body, some for the neck, and some were impossible to identify. The finished pieces were carried by a large machine to another area for assembly.

The family saw furkids sanding, varnishing, and putting strings on the instruments, while nearby, machines were doing the same work. Durkee's father spoke to a woman stringing thuralemms. In response, she picked up a completed instrument and began to play. It was obviously better sounding than the ones they had heard the night before in the marketplace. The children wondered whether better thuralemms were made by hand or by machine.

"That was beautiful," Mrs. Hart applauded.

Durkee's father and the musician smiled. He then said something to his son.

Durkee translated: "My father thanks you. He says

because everyone here does what they do best, the factory makes high quality thuralemms . . . and very many."

"Specialization," Mr. Hart contributed. "On Earth we call it specialization when everyone does what he or she does best. That way, we all have more of the best products to choose from."

"Yes," Durkee agreed. "Everybody is special. Some make thuralemms. Some make clothes. Some grow food. Everybody is special."

Once again John searched for the mastermind behind the furkid civilization. "Who plans all this?"

After a short conversation with his father, Durkee answered, "Everybody. If each person in the factory made thuralemms without help, then very few would be made. By cooperating, they are able to make many."

"But how about the rest of society?" John inquired. "How does everybody know what to do?"

Mr. Hart answered this question. "If each of us had to grow our own food, make our own clothes, and everything else, we all would be working harder and be much poorer. People specialize to become more wealthy."

They left the factory and walked outside into the sunlight. The area around the factory was beautifully landscaped with trees, large-leafed plants, and colorful flowers whose scent perfumed the air. All along the path, other stores and shops snuggled back into the forest. The scene was even more fascinating to the Harts because the plant forms were unlike anything they had ever seen.

Mr. Hart asked, "Durkee, does it ever get cold

here?" Durkee seemed unsure so John restated his question. "Do you ever have to wear more clothes?"

"Oh, yes," Durkee replied. "Later, many days later."

"That's very interesting," Mr. Hart observed as he looked at his watch. "The length of a day here is almost identical to that on Earth. This world is looking more and more like ours. Even their biology seems the same."

"Biology?" Durkee repeated.

"Biology is the study of plants and animals," Elizabeth explained.

Durkee apparently understood most of the discussion. He turned to a flower and breathed deep of its fragrance.

"Yes," he commented, "flowers need us."

"I've never thought of it that way," Elizabeth replied. "I thought *we* needed *flowers*."

John was tired of mysteries and riddles and just rolled his eyes at Durkee's statement. He decided he didn't particularly care to find out what Durkee was talking about.

Elizabeth's curiosity was still active, however. "Did you plant that flower?"

"No, it just grew."

"Then why does it need you?"

"No," he corrected, "it doesn't need *me*. *All* plants need animals. Animals need plants, too. They take in what we put out. We take in," he took a deep breath, "what they give out," and he let his breath out.

"He's talking about the oxygen cycle," Mrs. Hart told her children. "Plants give off oxygen and take in carbon dioxide. Animals, humans and furkids do just the opposite. We really need each other."

"It's a circle." Durkee made a sweeping motion with his arm. "There are many circles. Even the thuralemm factory is part of a circle. They're everywhere."

"Oh no," John half groaned and gave in. "Okay, I'll ask. What circle is the factory part of? Does the factory breathe?"

"No," Durkee said thoughtfully, "I don't think so. Owners of factories and shops pay us to work for them. Then we buy things from factories and shops. Just like a big circle." He finished by swinging his four-fingered hand in the air again.

"It's the same way on Earth," Mrs. Hart assured Durkee.

John was disappointed that their search for leaders again had not paid off, but he decided to keep his feelings to himself. "I see," he said without much enthusiasm.

"I'm not so sure I do." Elizabeth sounded confused. "Aren't businesses made up of people . . . or furkids?"

"That's true, Elizabeth, and a good point," her father praised her. "In a way, everyone is a little business. We sell our work and ideas, just as businesses sell goods and services. It's the way both our worlds operate."

John was trying not to sound too impatient. "Is this important?"

"Yes, it is," Mrs. Hart said seriously.

"But will it help us find glass marbles?" John's voice betrayed his frustration.

His parents knew exactly how he felt.

Mr. Hart put his hand on his son's shoulder. "It

might. Don't worry, son, we'll find an answer. We just need to keep looking."

Chapter Seven

PRICE SIGNALS

The thuralemm factory was located in an industri-
alized area, so Mr. and Mrs. Hart decided it would be
a good time to explore the various stores in hope of
finding the parts needed to repair the Apollo. They
wandered along the path, peering into shop windows
at the variety of products.

"What's the name of your planet, Durkee?" John
asked.

"Its called Mises, which means *free,*" he responded.

The shops were not much different from those on
Earth. Of course, many unfamiliar things were for sale.
Food stores were most fascinating since all the items
were different from Earth food. The children would
gladly have stayed longer if their parents had not insisted it was more important to continue their search
for the glass spheres.

Elizabeth discovered a model aircraft in a toy store.
Durkee confirmed that flying machines other than
hovercraft were to be found on Mises, but they didn't
find marbles in any store.

As they continued their walk through the village
they saw every kind of store imaginable. There were

stores that sold boats, stores that sold jewelry, and even stores that sold only laptop computers. John and Elizabeth were surprised to find as many different stores as there are on Earth. They had never really thought about the complicated system that provided so many products. John still suspected there was a planner who told the furkids what to make, but whenever he asked, people just answered, "I want to," or, "I make money by doing it."

Mr. and Mrs. Hart found several stores that carried complicated machinery, and they asked Durkee to question those shopkeepers about glass ball bearings. Almost all had heard of metal ball bearings but none had heard of glass ones.

The Harts had walked down one side of the path and back up the other. When they returned to the thuralemm factory they stopped to rest.

Suddenly John burst out, "I've got it!"

"What have you got this time?" Elizabeth asked tiredly. "Not the measles, I hope."

"No, I'm not sick," John scowled, "but I think I know the solution to our problem."

"What is it?" Mrs. Hart asked curiously.

"Everything has a price. I'm sure if we had enough money, someone would make the marbles we need to get home," John offered.

Durkee's antennae twitched as he tried to follow John's rapid speech.

"How about that, Durkee?" Elizabeth asked. "Do you think someone would make our marbles if we paid them enough?"

"Of course," Durkee answered.

"How much would it cost?" John asked.

"That depends," Durkee responded. "If someone chose to make marbles, it would mean they couldn't make something else. You see, the real cost of making something is the things they could have made, but did not. Each producer must decide if a product's price and quantity sold will cover all the costs."

"You mean," John asked, "the cost of making our marbles is really what the producer would give up in order to make the marbles?"

"Yes," Durkee replied, "that's one way to look at it."

"Well," Elizabeth said, "do you think they would take on those costs for us?"

"Only if the price were right," replied Durkee.

The children wondered if they could possibly get enough money to pay for the marbles they so desperately needed.

It was time for lunch and the family was getting hungry. Mealtime for the furkids and the Harts didn't always occur at the same time. Both had breakfast, but the furkids ate at least five more times a day. Their meals were smaller, but they had lots of them. Durkee's parents were having a picnic at the thuralemm factory and asked the Harts if they would like to join them. The food was different, but the family enjoyed the time with their new friends.

After lunch Mr. and Mrs. Hart went back to the Apollo with Durkee's mother, and the children spent the rest of the day at Durkee's house being entertained by his games and gadgets. While Mrs. Hart checked the mechanical and electronic systems, Mr. Hart used the computer to determine the exact time the comet would be in position for an attempt to fly through it.

The afternoon flew by quickly, and when Mr. and Mrs. Hart returned to Durkee's house it was time for supper. Then they all took showers, and while Elizabeth and John loved the little shower stalls, their parents had to stoop to get their heads under the water. Nevertheless, they were glad to change into the fresh clothes they had brought from the Apollo.

Everyone was in a good mood for the concert they planned to attend that evening. Although the Harts could not forget their difficult situation, they all looked forward to this event and decided not to dwell on the cost of not repairing the Apollo, which was growing higher and higher. It could mean never seeing Earth again—a high cost indeed.

They walked to the concert hall since the evening was warm and the hall was not too far away. It was fun to see all the starbirds and furkids also going to the concert. So many families of glowing starbirds floated along, looking like balloons full of fireflies, that the lights along the path were unnecessary. Furkids and starbirds stared at the alien family and whispered as they walked past. The concert hall was the biggest building the Harts had seen on Mises. Shaped like a giant dome, it reminded them of a football stadium.

As their group made its way down the ticket line, John asked Durkee, "How do they know how much to charge for tickets?"

"We tell them. Everybody tells them. They just charge as much as they can."

"They do?" John wondered. "If they are trying to

make as much money as possible, then the tickets must be very expensive."

"Oh no," Durkee answered quickly. "They charge the right price. If the tickets cost too much, nobody would buy them. Then they wouldn't make *any* money."

Elizabeth was interested. "Why do you say the *right* price? It would seem just as 'right' to me if they charged less."

"Well," Durkee answered, "I wouldn't mind paying less, but if the price were too low we might not be able to get into the concert. All the tickets would already be sold."

"Why is that?" Elizabeth inquired.

Durkee tried to explain. "If the price is too low, then everyone would want to go, and there aren't enough seats for everyone. Besides, if they didn't charge enough, they couldn't pay the orchestra what they want, and then no one would play. If they didn't play, then no one could go to a concert because there would be no concert. You see, without prices, how would you decide who should get things? Would you decide because of the color of their hair, or their height, or by how many fingers they have?"

John loved to make money, so he really thought about Durkee's insights on cost and price. They thanked Durkee's parents for buying their tickets and all walked into the excitement and bustle of the hall.

Chapter Eight

THE STOPLIGHTS OF THE SYSTEM

Durkee's family and the Harts were escorted down to the first row of seats. The owners of the hall meant this to honor the Harts, but it also gave the family room for their legs. In the regular seats they would have been forced to sit cramped up with their knees in their faces.

The furkid orchestra was already on stage tuning their instruments, many of which were thuralemms. The other instruments were unfamiliar. Some spiraled up around the heads of their players. One instrument was like a big round ball with a little mouthpiece which contained the keys sticking out of its side. Some horns had strings inside their tubes; the furkids who played these looked as if they were blowing up bird cages.

The starbird choir floated above the orchestra, while the starbirds in the audience hovered over their seats as they chatted with their furkid friends.

Durkee explained that the starbirds whistling was impossible for furkids to reproduce, and the furkid language was outside the starbirds' range. Although neither could speak the other's language, they understood each other very well. The Harts had suspected

69

as much.

The concert hall resounded with the two languages. The excitement was so intense the family didn't need antennae to feel it. As the concert hall continued to fill, John took the opportunity to continue the discussion with Durkee. "Isn't someone on Mises running and planning things? I understand how ticket prices are set, but it seems to me there should be a lot more to it. I just can't figure it out. I get the feeling your leaders must be hiding. Maybe they're bad or afraid or something."

Elizabeth added softly, "Isn't there someone who decides how much of something to produce, how many concerts to give, how much food to grow, or how many hovercrafts to make?"

"Can I ask you a few questions first?"

"Fire away, Durkee," John told him.

"What do you call selling something for more money than it costs to produce it?"

Mr. Hart answered, "We call that making a profit."

"Then what do you call producing something that costs more than you can sell for?"

"That's taking a loss."

"Okay," Durkee stated, "profit and loss tell everyone how much of everything to produce."

"But is it really that easy?" John asked. "Profit and loss can't talk."

John's statement caused Durkee's antennae to twitch wildly. "Yes, they do. They are economic talk— the language of the economic system. They are the reason individuals produce as much as they do."

Mr. Hart nodded.

"Do you believe that, Dad?" John asked. "Tell me again what you mean, Durkee. I don't understand."

Durkee rubbed his chin the same way Mr. Hart did when he was thinking. "Pretend you were selling those marble things you are looking for. If each made a profit, wouldn't you want to sell as many as possible?"

"Oh!" Elizabeth said. "I think I see. The producer decides."

"Correct." Durkee grinned. "The amount of profit shows when to produce more. If there is profit, you can be sure someone will produce more."

John asked, "Are losses as important as profits, then?"

"Of course," Durkee explained. "A loss means cost is greater than revenue. With a loss, we should either lower our cost or raise the price, or both. And if that doesn't work, then maybe we shouldn't produce it at all."

"You're saying that profit and loss are like signals that tell us how much to produce?" John concluded.

"Right again," Durkee smiled. "As long as you can get more from selling your product than it costs to produce it, the signal is to produce more."

"What about the salary you pay yourself?" Elizabeth asked. "Isn't that profit?"

"No, salary is part of the cost," Durkee said. "Profits are what's left after all costs are paid. Profits are wonderful. They provide savings and tools, and they tell producers how much everyone wants. So profits are very important. But losses are important, too. Profit and loss make sure everything is used efficiently."

"And all this time," John commented thoughtfully,

"I believed people just went into business to make money. I appreciate your taking the time to explain it all, Durkee."

"But, son," Mr. Hart spoke up, "people do go into business to make money. Its just that prices and costs show us which business is the best one to start."

Just then a small gray-haired furkid in a black cape walked onto the stage and the audience became quiet. The concert was about to begin.

Durkee whispered that the conductor was very famous—part artist, part virtuoso, and known all over Mises. The crowd applauded and the starbirds made low fluttery whistles like the cooing of a thousand doves. The conductor turned to the audience, bowed, turned back to the orchestra, and raised his arms. The audience became totally silent. He brought his arms down and the symphony began.

The Harts were overwhelmed with the wondrous sounds of the soft, beautiful music. The arrangement tenderly reflected the new world they had entered. As the orchestra grew louder the starbird choir broke into song. The vast range of their voices was unlike anything the Harts had ever heard. Tingles ran up and down John's spine. He looked at his sister and saw goose bumps on her arms, too. He knew she was enjoying the music and he smiled to see her so full of life. The concert, several short pieces and one long symphony, went on for most of the evening. The Harts were entranced by the music which ended much too quickly. The audience applauded for a long, long time. Life on Mises could have offered no moment more beautiful, and at least for a while, the Harts had been able to forget their problems.

"That was beautiful," Elizabeth sighed. "How did they become so good?"

Durkee answered, "My father used to play in this orchestra. I'll ask him." He spoke to his father and translated the answer: "My father says they are so good because the leader hires only the very best players. He says he's a pretty good musician, but a better one took his place."

"Oh, that's too bad," Elizabeth was sorry. "Is your father sad he lost his job?"

Again Durkee translated the answer: "My father says *you* would be sad if he were still playing."

The whole family laughed at the joke. Durkee waited until the chuckling had faded.

"My father was telling more than a joke. It is true. The head of the orchestra found someone who was a better musician. He did it for the koereadum."

"What's a koereadum?" John asked.

"Koereadum is the orchestra. For the best music, the leader always looks for the most talented musicians."

The crowd was beginning to leave the concert hall. The two families got up and started to make their way to the door.

"What did your father do when he lost his position with the koereadum?" Mrs. Hart asked.

"Father thought about teaching music. But Mother is smart in business, and so they decided to see if they could make thuralemms better than Father played them. Now their thuralemms are well known. Some of those used in tonight's concert were produced in my parents koereadum."

"In your parents koereadum?" John questioned. "I thought koereadum meant orchestra."

"It does, it does. Businesses and orchestras are both koereadums."

The children were perplexed. Elizabeth asked, "Why do you use the same word for orchestras and businesses?"

"They are much the same," Durkee told them. "In both, many people work together for the same purpose. The orchestra leader looks for those who are very good at making thuralemms so the thuralemms will be very good, as good as the music tonight."

"It's still pretty peculiar," John said.

"Well," Durkee said, "those who work at the thuralemm factory try to do a good job, because they will get more money if they are worth more to the factory. Musicians also try to do a good job, because the leader of the orchestra wants to make the best music so others will buy tickets. It is in everyone's . . ." Durkee searched for a word, "self-interest to make good music and good thuralemms."

"But all the musicians played and sang together so well. Is cooperation the same thing as competition?" Elizabeth asked.

"In a way, yes," Durkee affirmed. "Of course, the players love the music, and most thuralemm factory workers like what they do, but they both want to be paid as much as possible for their work. To be the very best, to make the most money, they must play music together or make thuralemms together. They compete to be the ones who cooperate best. They have to be good, or no one would buy tickets or thuralemms. We would all be out of business."

"Koereadums," Mrs. Hart mused.

"Isn't it nice?" Durkee asked.

"What's nice?" Mrs. Hart inquired.

"That all the things we need and want, and all the things we buy and use, exist because it is good for those who make them."

At Durkee's house the children lay in bed thinking. If the system worked as Durkee said it did, then some-one should be willing to make marbles for the Apollo.

In their sleep, they dreamed of furkids and orchestras . . . and of their home in Honolulu.

Chapter Nine

PROFITS AND PRIVILEGES

When the Harts woke up in Durkee's house the second morning, they felt more comfortable with their strange surroundings. Mr. and Mrs. Hart continued to ask Durkee and his parents questions about their planet, hoping to find help. John was getting ready for breakfast when he noticed Elizabeth wasn't out of bed yet.

"That's funny," he thought. "Elizabeth is usually the first one up. I'll go get her."

Elizabeth was not easy to wake this morning. John shook her several times before she would even acknowledge him. Satisfied that she was awake, he left her and sat down at the low round table for breakfast.

While they ate, Durkee's father told the Harts of a well known furkid named Hayek who lived alone in a home built into the side of a cliff just outside the village. Everyone respectfully referred to the elder as the Old One, and although he seldom came into town, his advice was often sought to settle disputes between villagers.

John was surprised when Elizabeth still was not up. Mr. Hart went to get her this time. She must have fallen back to sleep as soon as John left the room.

Mr. Hart gently shook her. "Elizabeth, wake up or you'll miss breakfast."

"I'm not hungry," she said and closed her eyes.

"Come on, we have to get going."

"Okay," she said grudgingly. "I'm awake now."

As she swung her feet to the floor, she asked her father, "What's all the noise? That ambulance sounds real close."

"You must still be dreaming," her father told her. "Get dressed and come eat something. We're going into the country today."

Elizabeth wandered to the breakfast table a few minutes later, still half asleep. She didn't talk at all and only picked at her food. When everyone had finished, Durkee and the Harts got into the hovercraft and headed for the home of the Old One.

After a few minutes Elizabeth asked, "Could I put my head in your lap, Mom? I feel a little funny."

"You look a little funny, too. Too much excitement, I suppose," she told her as she lay down.

"Don't you hear that siren, Mom?" she asked.

"No," Mrs. Hart said, "I don't hear anything like a siren. Maybe your ears are still ringing from the starbird choir."

"Listen." Elizabeth yawned. "It's getting louder." With that statement she fell asleep again.

Durkee turned around to ask Mrs. Hart, "What is this siren Elizabeth heard?"

"Oh, it's probably nothing. She's just tired."

Durkee seemed upset. "Is this a siren?" he asked, and he made a high shrill sound.

"Yes, that's a siren," Mr. Hart confirmed. "How did you know?"

Durkee's eyes grew big and he brought the hovercraft to an abrupt halt. "How long has Elizabeth been hearing the siren?"

"Well, she first mentioned it when I woke her up," Mr. Hart answered.

Durkee became rigid. "Hang on!" he cried, and the hovercraft shot forward at a much faster pace.

He turned around long enough to tell the Harts, "Elizabeth has a sickness that furkids get once in a while. It is called bertoff maredore, which means siren sickness, because whoever gets the sickness hears that sound before they die."

"Before they die!" John was first to exclaim. "What do you mean? Is Liz going to die?"

Elizabeth raised her head when John shouted her name. She murmured, "Who's going to die?" Then, just as quickly, she passed out.

"All furkids know what the siren in the head means, and they go to the swamp immediately when they hear it. We have lost time already." Durkee turned back to concentrate on piloting the hovercraft.

They flew like the wind along a path with many forks and turns. The Harts saw no signs, but there must have been some because Durkee knew which of several paths to take as they sped along.

The Harts re-checked their seat belts. John was sitting in front with Durkee while Mr. and Mrs. Hart seemed to be speaking frantically in the back seat. John couldn't hear what they were saying but he knew they were very concerned. Durkee was silent as he squinted straight ahead. He spoke only once when he took the telephone from the front of the hovercraft to call someone for assistance.

John decided to sit still and be brave. He clutched the sides of the hovercraft in case they took a sharp corner. When he looked back at his sister, he became even more frightened. She looked as though she were about to die, and with each glance she looked worse. She was perspiring great drops and moaning. John never worried much about death, but this was his sister! He suddenly realized how much he loved her, and his mind raced over the times he had been unkind. Feeling sorry about some of the things he had said, he knew it was too late to retrieve his words. Elizabeth was desperately ill, and he only wanted to help her and tell her he was sorry.

The ride seemed to take forever. As the path straightened out Durkee drove even faster. John watched the countryside change from forest to jungle. The trees were bigger and stranger, and the whole world seemed darker. John heard a lonely cry from the jungle as he sank deep into his seat.

The jungle finally became a wetland and a fog fell upon them. John saw light reflecting off water among the trees, and several times he thought he saw eyes staring from the swamp. When the area became entirely swampy, Durkee slowed down. John didn't like the idea of stopping in this place, but then through the fog he spotted a group of large, shining buildings with a fence that extended as far as he could see into the fog.

They approached the complex, and Durkee drove

through the front gate which had opened automatically. Furkids dressed in white cloaks were waiting with a stretcher. Mr. and Mrs. Hart placed Elizabeth on it without a word, and they all went inside to a room where a large picture window faced the bleak unfriendly swamp. One of the white cloaked furkids said something to Durkee.

He turned to the family "We are lucky. They have succeeded in capturing a surissaluh. Unless they have problems, they will have it here in a few minutes and take from it that which kills. It will cure Elizabeth."

Just then one of the furkids pointed a finger out the window into the fog. John gasped. At first he thought he saw a dragon. As it came closer, he was able to see it was really a huge serpent with a dragon-like head. It was bigger around than his father and mother put together, and its head was wider than he could stretch his arms. Four green, bat-like wings grew directly behind its head where its shoulders should have been.

It was flapping its double set of wings at a terrific rate. Only the tip of its tail touched the ground as it towered into the air, three times as tall as Mr. Hart. John was so awestruck by the beast he had not noticed the three ropes around its head. Furkids in hovercraft were directing the unwilling surissaluh toward a concrete platform beneath the window.

The two furkids in each craft were wearing suits of shining protective armor. John thought of the knights in medieval times who fought the fire-breathing dragons. The surissaluh twisted and struggled, but the furkids kept it under control. The snakelike creature had two fangs, each at least as long as John's arm, and it thrashed its head toward the hovercraft at every opportunity, but the ropes prevented it from destroying them. Its body convulsed, strained, and dragged all three craft as it coiled to spring forward in an attempt to break free.

Eventually the furkids succeeded in getting the creature onto the platform and somehow held it still. Then another vehicle, a rolling tower, started toward the surissaluh. It was the first vehicle with wheels the family had seen on Mises. This tower was as tall as the serpent and housed a great pair of pincers designed to clamp below the creature's head.

As the tower approached, the surissaluh renewed its efforts to escape. The furkids turned their hovercraft motors off in order to use their weight as anchors to hold the squirming beast. The dragon snake hissed and snapped at its captors. The Harts could hear its protests through the heavy glass window.

The serpent became outraged when the tower reached it, its anger shining in its hideous orange eyes. The pincers attempted to close around its neck as it coiled down, but it shot back up and snapped the tower. The pincers opened again, and the furkids on the ropes tried to pull more tightly as the pincers closed, but the serpent again slipped away.

Within the compound, Elizabeth was tossing and turning nearly as much as the serpent. Her parents held her on the cot, looking up at the surissaluh only occasionally, but John's undivided attention was on the serpent. His knuckles grew white as the furkids failed to immobilize the creature. As if Elizabeth sensed their failure, she groaned loudly enough to distract John from the activity outside. Durkee was leaning against the window, staring at the battle taking place.

The pincers opened slowly for another try. The ropes maneuvered the snake into position, and the pincers started to close. As the serpent coiled away, the pincers were quickly reopened, and when the surissaluh sprang up, they clamped shut around their mark. The beast was bound.

It was furious, stretching its head like a harassed rat. The tail lifted off the ground, whipped though the air, and wrapped around the tower. John was afraid it was going to crush the furkids inside. The surissaluh coiled the end of its tail beneath the pincers and sprang with all its strength, so that the whole tower shook.

John was wondering what they were going to do with the thing when a trap door on top of the tower popped open. An armored furkid holding a glass container came out and looked directly into the eyes of the enraged beast. If the surissaluh could have moved, furkid, armor, and all would have been swallowed in one bite.

When the serpent snapped its jaws, the brave furkid quickly struck the bottle upward at one of the great fangs. It touched the sharp tooth for only a moment, then was held up to see if there was anything inside. Satisfied, the bottle holder disappeared back into the tower and came scurrying out the bottom.

The bottle was brought immediately to the technician, who measured out an exact portion and mixed it with water. She brought it to Elizabeth, who by now was gravely ill. With the help of Mr. and Mrs. Hart, she poured the mixture down Elizabeth's throat. She coughed and sputtered, but drank it all, and the effects were immediate. Elizabeth seemed to enter a deep, pleasant sleep.

The family finally relaxed, and the white-cloaked furkid moved them into a large reception room where they could wait comfortably until Elizabeth recovered. Durkee told them she would be ready to go by morning.

Durkee began to explain what had occurred: "The surissaluh is the only cure for siren sickness. Its poison must be absolutely fresh. Without it there would have been death. We are very lucky that the owners of the surissalluh captured one so quickly. The surissaluh are very hard to find and capture. They need much room to live, and they can leap great distances with the help of their wings. In the old days, before surissaluh were kept in compounds like this one, they would eat us and everyone feared them. If anyone got siren sickness, someone had to find a surissaluh and kill it. So surissaluh became scarce and many people died. Now the owners of the surissaluh compound take care of them and provide the cure for those who need it."

"It looked so dangerous," John observed. "How did it all start?"

"With an idea," Durkee told him. "The ones who started raising surissaluh bought this land and decided to find a way to produce medicine for everyone."

Mr. Hart told Durkee, "We owe them a great deal. They saved our daughter."

"It is funny, but when the owners first thought of the idea, many thought they were foolish. They said there was no way to handle the surissaluh. Others said it would be too dangerous to have so many surissaluh in one area, that they might escape."

"But they did it anyway?" John asked.

"Yes," Durkee explained. "It was their property. The good and bad things, the privileges and responsibilities, that came with it were theirs. They went into the business to help other people and themselves. They make a profit, of course."

"And they deserve it!" John said. "They saved Liz's life."

"The profit is the privilege," Durkee said. "The responsibility is also theirs. If their property, the surissaluh, escaped and hurt someone, they would be in trouble."

"What does 'private property' mean on Mises?" Mr. Hart was curious.

"Simple," Durkee said. "Anything you own is yours to treat in any way you want, as long as it doesn't interfere with someone else's private property. If the surissaluh were to eat me, that would be interfering with my most important private property. If the owners couldn't keep the profit from a surissaluh ranch, then things wouldn't be done as well as they are now. Why else would anyone play around with such beasts?"

"You're right, Durkee," Mr. Hart concurred. "Come to think of it, you have the freedom to choose because you are free to own."

"That's right," said Durkee. "They take care of the surissaluh because they own them. The surissaluh are better off, and so are we. Everyone benefits because of private property."

The Harts spent the rest of the day watching holovision. The machine projected three-dimensional scenes into what looked like a large fish tank. They viewed movies about ancient times on Mises and other programs that were very mysterious. Durkee finally found a musical show the family enjoyed.

Later that evening, white-cloaked furkids brought in trays of food and showed them where they could sleep. One of them talked to Durkee and gave him a piece of paper. After Durkee examined the paper, he took a little round stone out of his pouch. He pressed the stone to an ink-pad and then to the paper, leaving an imprint. The furkid gave him a copy of the paper and left. While they were eating Mr. Hart asked Durkee about the paper.

"It's a promise to the owners of the surissaluh," he told them. "I have promised to pay them for the medicine. You can pay me back with your share of the money from the tours of your spaceship. We really promised to pay when we accepted the treatment, though."

"But how can you promise something before you see what you are getting?" John asked.

"Some things don't have to be said to be understood," Durkee told him. "If you were in a burning building way up high, and someone was on the ground with a net, would you make them promise not to move before you jumped?"

"No," John admitted, "I suppose not."

"Who would be wrong if the net was moved?"

"Why, they would," John reasoned.

"On Earth we call promises contracts," Mrs. Hart pointed out.

"Contract." Durkee tried the word. "Contracts. Contracts are because of private property, too. They are a way of dealing with the things that are yours."

"But catching someone in a net is not like selling private property!" John spoke as if this insight had come like a flash of lightning.

"But your most important private property is you, and you can contract or promise to do all sorts of things. My parents' factory is on property owned by others. The owners have a contract with my parents because they use the property."

"What if someone doesn't do what the contract says, or hurts someone else?" John asked.

"It's really the same thing," Durkee told him. "It all comes down to someone who violates property rights. You must remember that *you* are your most important property. On Mises, our law says you can do anything except disturb another's private property or contracts."

Mr. Hart commented, "The word *law* tells me there is some form of authority on Mises."

"We do have agreements," Durkee said. "We agree not to interfere with anybody else's private property unless we have a contract."

"That's the only law you have?" Mrs. Hart asked disbelievingly. "But how do you handle criminals?"

"Criminals are those who disturb private property without permission. We take them to court."

"Ah ha!" Mr. Hart said. "You have courts. There is somebody in charge."

"What do you mean?" Durkee was confused.

"I mean, you do have a government," Mr. Hart tried to explain.

"Only if someone breaks the law." Durkee shrugged and fingered an antenna. "We have rights, but most of them are just understood and accepted. Some are because of promises or contracts we make. If someone does violate another's rights, then the courts are where we go to figure out what to do about it. But I don't know why you would say courts are in charge."

"Maybe you're right, Durkee," Mrs. Hart commented. "Back on Earth, our history is full of times when the courts were the only ones that determined people's right to their property."

Durkee smiled. "Tomorrow, when Elizabeth is ready, we will go to see the Old One. Some of us hire him to be a court. You can ask him these questions. I don't know much about rights, but I know you have them whether you realize it or not. Making contracts and not being hit in the face are both private property rights. We have set up courts to handle times when these rights are violated."

"This sounds familiar, doesn't it?" Mr. Hart observed.

"It sure does," Mrs. Hart agreed. "Sounds like life, liberty, and the pursuit of happiness. We hold these truths to be self-evident—yes, very familiar indeed."

Chapter Ten

ALL ABOUT MONEY

True to Durkee's word, Elizabeth was ready to travel by morning. Wanting to hear everything that had happened, she was disappointed she hadn't been able to see the surissaluh. As the hovercraft made its way through the scenic Mises landscape, they finally left the swamp and entered forests similar to those around Durkee's village. Watching the exotic plants, trees, and animals kept the children occupied. When Durkee noticed clouds forming, he pushed a button to move a transparent plastic bubble around them, and soon it rained.

As they passed through a particularly beautiful valley, Durkee slowed the skimmer. One side of the valley was formed by a chain of rugged hills; the other was a steep cliff covered with ivy-like plants. The only break in the cliff was a fissure with a stream flowing from it. They skimmed across an open field and made their way around boulders and bushes until they reached the crack in the cliff.

Durkee parked the skimmer, walked up to the rock wall, and vanished from sight. The Harts were surprised to see, carved into the rock, a steep stairway that followed the stream up the cliff.

Durkee, a few steps above them, yelled, "Follow me," and motioned the Harts to climb the steps. At one point they passed a small water wheel but were unable to tell where the harnessed power was being directed. The sliver of light above them grew bigger, and the stairway turned into a ledge that ran along the side of the cliff and overlooked the valley. The hovercraft below looked like a tiny toy. Although the path was wide, everyone hugged the wall to avoid the edge of the cliff.

The trail abruptly ended at the round, dark entrance to a tunnel that led straight into the rock wall. The children weren't excited about entering the blackness but followed as Durkee and their parents disappeared inside. They had gone about thirty yards when they saw in the distance a torch fastened to the wall. As they walked toward it, their eyes adjusted to the dark and the tunnel became a lot less spooky. They walked past the torch, and when it was nearly out of sight, another appeared in front of them, and when that was almost out of sight, they saw a third. The torches were positioned so that one was always visible. As they approached the third torch they saw a large wooden door with a grotesque knocker.

Durkee stepped up and banged on the door. They listened, but there was no reply. He knocked again, this time much louder and longer. Then they heard someone on the other side, working the latch. The door opened slightly and an eye peered out. The voice that went with the suspicious eye asked Durkee a question.

Durkee said to the family, "He wants to know if we

are selling something."

The eye moved to the rest of the party. When it saw the Harts it became huge and the door swung open. There stood a little old gray-haired furkid wearing a dark cloak with a hood. He took Durkee's hand and nearly yanked him off his feet as he pulled him through the door. Then he tugged and urged the Harts to enter. Expecting the cave to be dark and wet with bare walls, they were amazed to find a bright, cheery, marvelous little home. The walls were decorated with tapestries, paintings, and photographs. The ceiling contained a domed glass skylight which shone with falling raindrops.

The Old One said something and Durkee translated: "The Old One says he has heard much about the alien visitors that have come to our planet. He knows you are looking for a game you play with little glass balls. He feels honored you have come to visit him."

The Old One motioned for the family to sit on the soft stools around the room. He put a log on the fire.

"Tell the Old One we are glad to be his guests," Mr. Hart said, "but we didn't come to Mises for a vacation. We are shipwrecked and need help."

John said, "Ask him to take us to your leader."

Durkee translated everything for the Old One. The gray furkid listened and asked Durkee questions. While the two carried on their conversation, the Old One made tea by heating water at the fireplace and pouring it through dried leaves into cups. Happily, he offered it to the family.

When they all had drinks, Durkee said, "I have told him about the parts you need for the Apollo and that you want to meet our leaders. He cannot help you find our leaders. I think maybe the Old One is a leader. He will gladly help if he can."

Mr. Hart thought he knew how to help find the Mises government, so he asked, "Who helps your poor?"

Durkee translated and gave the Old One's response to the Harts. "He would like to know just who the 'poor' are."

"Someone without very much money," John quickly replied.

Durkee conferred again with the Old One, then said, "The Old One says he doesn't have much money, so he must be the 'poor.' But he doesn't want any help."

"No, no," John protested. "You know someone is poor when they don't have all the things they want, and you feel sorry for them."

Durkee talked to the Old One again. Then he asked, John, "Do you have everything you want?"

"No, but I'm not poor."

Durkee told the gray furkid John's answer. Both furkids looked puzzled. Finally, after talking at length, Durkee asked, "Is money part of your religion? It seems very important to you that everyone should have the same amount."

"No!" Mrs. Hart boldly stated. "We know that different things make people happy. What we would like to know is whether you have some sort of organization that takes care of emergencies. For example, who takes care of furkids who don't have enough to eat or a place to stay?"

Durkee talked to the Old One. "The Old One understands now. He could not understand the word *poor* because almost everyone wants more of something. The Old One came out here to study and rest. He chose to be rich by making his wants few. He was poor for peace and quiet, not money. Besides, even today's very poorest are richer than most furkids of the really olden days. Is it that way in your world, too?"

"Yes, it is," Mrs. Hart told him. "But who takes care of those needing assistance?"

"We do," Durkee stated.

"But don't you have laws and agencies to help those furkids?" John insisted.

Durkee consulted the Old One and then turned to John, "If we didn't want to help them, why would we pass a law to make us do something we don't want to do?" Durkee waited a moment before continuing. "Besides, it would take all the fun out of providing things for someone if we *had* to help them."

"Who helps the needy in your world, John?" asked Durkee.

"Government," came the reply.

"Does your government also provide counsel, hope, and personal caring?" Durkee inquired.

"Not really," said John.

"We on Mises believe that giving money without requiring personal responsibility is irresponsible. Do you think that helping someone to become helpless is really an act of kindness?" asked Durkee.

"Probably not," John said.

The family enjoyed their tea as Durkee and the Old One talked over the Harts' problems. Later the Old One brought them a lunch of more tea and seeds hollowed out and filled with a paste that tasted much like catsup.

As they relaxed in the Old One's cave, other hovercraft were gathering at the foot of the cliff next to the stone stairway. Elizabeth and John decided to go exploring. They walked out into the long dark tunnel that led away from the Old One's home. They were not frightened this time and enjoyed discovering things in the passageway. They noticed little gold flecks in the rock and once in a while saw a piece of colored gemstone. Elizabeth was walking along, looking up at the cold, damp walls when a whistle blew next to her foot.

"*What was that?!*" she shrieked.

John's face showed his surprise in the torchlight. "I don't know. Here, grab my hand."

"Who whistled?" Elizabeth questioned in the dark.

Then another softer whistle came from the same location.

"It might be some sort of animal," John suggested.

"Be careful, John," Elizabeth cautioned as John knelt down beside a rock. As he reached out to pick it up, it whistled again.

"That's no rock," he said, just as the thing sprouted legs and jumped off like a frog.

The young people looked at each other, shrugged their shoulders, and continued down the tunnel. Elizabeth came to the opening first and looked over the edge of the cliff.

"John, come quick. Something's going on down by Durkee's skimmer."

John ran to the ledge and peered over. "No kidding. Look, they're carrying something . . . maybe weapons. Looks like they're going to climb up here."

"Let's tell Durkee," Elizabeth said, and they ran down the stone hall.

Scurrying through the wooden door, they announced the arrival of the unexpected visitors. It took a moment for the Old One to understand the reason for their excitement. Then he explained that the furkids were coming to meet the Harts and bring them gifts. The Harts were wondering why visitors would come to see them when a loud knock sounded at the heavy door. The Old One threw it open, and in they came— all ten of them—each holding a present.

For the next few hours the family answered hundreds of questions, with Durkee translating as fast as he could. The guests wanted to know everything there was to know about Earth. They were most interested in space travel. They had not done any themselves and couldn't believe Earthlings had really walked on the moon.

The visitors also were interested in Mr. Hart's mustache, and all wanted to touch it. Elizabeth and Mrs. Hart's long hair was also the source of a lot of admiration since the furkids own hair remained short and curly. In response, the Harts complimented the furkids on their beautiful blue, purple, and gray pelts. This greatly pleased them because the grooming of their colorful woolly coats was a matter of pride. The most respected color was the gray that came with age.

When enough questions had been asked to satisfy everyone's curiosity, the Old One brought out the food he had prepared when the Harts first arrived. No one seemed surprised that he had fixed enough for the whole noisy crowd.

After the meal, the Harts were presented with gifts from the visitors, who represented ten different villages. All the articles were unusually beautiful. One was a small pyramid made from red crystal-like ruby, its edge decorated with gold metal. There was a silver ball that changed colors like the northern lights when picked up, and a cube of hollow rock that when held, made the person's heartbeat loud enough for everyone to hear. The Harts passed it around and listened to everyone's heart. Another present was a clear crystal ball in which, when held at a certain angle, a beautiful flower appeared. One gift was a very plain-looking rock, like any you could pick up along the road, but this one rang a bell-like note when it was squeezed.

One egg-shaped object had an opening into which one looked and saw the entire room, even the area almost directly in back of the viewer. A vase was presented that looked like a delicately carved masterpiece. The Harts were amazed to learn it was naturally shaped that way. Everyone appreciated the tearshaped piece of glass with a rainbow inside, and the sea shell that made the sound of a thousand bells when it was put to one's ear. The last gift was a big diamond with a gold nugget deep within it.

The family asked Durkee to thank all the guests for their kind generosity. But just as the Harts began to examine their gifts more closely, the group rose, said hasty good-byes, and left as quickly as they had arrived.

"My goodness," Mrs. Hart commented, "what an exciting way to spend an afternoon. Perhaps we should divide these unusual gifts among us so we can all have our favorites. They'll make lovely keepsakes.

"That's a great idea," Mr. Hart agreed. "How should we do it, though?"

"I've got an idea," Elizabeth suggested. "Since we've talked a lot about money, why don't we buy the ones we want?"

"That'll work," Mr. Hart said. "We'll start with the same amount of play money for each of us. Then we'll bid for each item. We can buy whatever we want. If we really want a particular gift, we can spend whatever it takes to get it, even if it means using all our money. If we want a lot of different gifts, we can spread our money out and buy the ones nobody else wants.

Durkee and the Old One followed this discussion with interest. Durkee tried to translate everything for the gray furkid. He must have done a good job, because the Old One went to the fireplace mantle for several handfuls of tiny round seashells that looked like coins. He also grabbed a tall basket with a wide bottom that closed to a small hole in its top. Mr. Hart divided the discs into four equal piles, one for each member of the family.

Mrs. Hart said, "We will bid on the gifts one at a time. When you win the auction, you must drop the number of discs you bid into the basket. We can practice a few times to get the hang of it."

"Who will give one disc for this?" Mr. Hart held up a gift. Everyone was willing to give up one disc. "How about two?" John dropped out of the bidding. It seemed to take only three or four discs to buy a gift, and all were bid on and bought.

John spent all his discs on the ruby pyramid and wasn't too happy about not having a chance to bid on other things. Elizabeth was more conservative and had discs left over. She decided she should bid more next time.

Then they emptied the basket and started over. Durkee and the Old One smiled a lot as they watched the Harts play this game. Sometimes they even had to hold in their laughter.

The bidding started a second time. Something funny seemed to be happening. Instead of three or four discs to buy an item, it was taking five or six. And at the end, each member had more discs left over than they had the first time.

"How strange," Mr. Hart observed. "The prices seem to be going up. Let's start over." Mr. Hart checked the inside of the basket to make sure there were no discs stuck to the sides. By this time Durkee and the Old One were positively giggling.

The discs were separated into four piles again, and the bidding began for a third time. But the family was growing suspicious. Now the price of a gift had gone up to eight or nine shells, and Durkee and the gray furkid were almost falling off their stools with laughter. The Harts turned to stare at their hosts.

The two furkids slowly calmed down, and Durkee stopped giggling long enough to say, "I will show you something." He asked Elizabeth to hold one of the discs in her fist and wait.

"What's supposed to happen?" she asked, She sat silently for a minute, then squealed, "Hey! It moved!"

She opened her hand. Where there had been one disc, now there were two. Quickly the other Harts picked up discs and tried the same trick, with identical results.

"They're alive," Durkee told them. "They live around streams. One disc will divide into two, but only in the dark. Every time you put them in the basket, most of them reproduced."

"Amazing," John said.

"On Earth, we call that inflation," Mrs. Hart said with a twinkle.

"But," John protested, "I thought inflation happens because prices go up."

"What happened when you spent all your discs on

one item?" Mr. Hart asked.

"Well, I couldn't buy anything else."

"So the prices of the other items went down because we didn't have to bid against you. Isn't that right?" Mrs. Hart questioned.

"Hmmmmm." John pondered the situation. "That's right. But then how does inflation happen?"

Mr. Hart explained. "The same way it just happened to us. When a government prints a batch of money, but the economy doesn't produce more goods, the price of everything goes up. Money becomes worth less, just as the shells are worth less because there are so many of them now. After all, printing money doesn't create things we can use; only individuals can do that. And just because there is more money, it doesn't mean there are more things to buy."

"That means," Elizabeth commented, "that governments can print more money any time they want to."

Durkee looked very concerned. "That must be nice for the ones who print money and spend it, but what about those like the Old One who have saved money all their lives? When prices go up, the value of their money is destroyed." Durkee paused and rubbed his chin. "Why do you let them print extra money?"

"Good question, Durkee." Mr. Hart wondered, too.

Chapter Eleven

OPEN FOR BUSINESS

After a night of sleeping on mats at the Old One's, the family awakened to the sun streaming through the skylight ceiling of the cave. They got ready for another day of uncovering clues that they hoped would make the Apollo airworthy again. Durkee and the Old One seemed more excited about the search than were the Harts.

Of course, the Harts were not allowed to leave without a hearty breakfast. While John and Elizabeth borrowed a bag to carry their gifts, Mr. and Mrs. Hart spoke quietly of the deadline for their takeoff.

After talking to the Old One, Durkee stood up, walked to the center of the room, and officially announced, "The Old One has decided to help you. He will go with us."

"Uh . . . good," Mr. Hart muttered as he looked at his wife. Secretly, they wondered how much help the old furkid would be. Such thinking caused both furkids antennae to turn. The family felt the two creatures knew their exact thoughts.

The old furkid started to speak again, but Durkee did not translate. Instead, he took out a notebook and made a list with a long electrical pen. When he had filled several pages, he told the family they were ready to go. They all left the cave, went down the stone staircase to Durkee's skimmer, and were off again. The family felt helpless. The furkids were carrying on a nonstop conversation with no translation offered. Although they enjoyed the ride, the family knew they were not heading back to Durkee's village.

"Where are we going?" Mr. Hart quizzed.

"The Old One is going to show you how to get the parts to fix your ship," Durkee answered and then smiled. "He is very creative. Just wait. You'll see."

Mr. Hart leaned back in his seat, but he could not relax.

"Try not to worry, dear," Mrs. Hart whispered. "They haven't led us wrong yet. Besides, they might really give us some helpful information."

As they traveled farther and farther away from the green forests, the landscape became dry and hot, like a desert. There were hardly any trees and only a few bushes spread thinly about the hard, dry ground. Durkee left the path and took off across the barren terrain without looking at a map or using a compass. The hotter it became, the more the Harts missed the green of the forest.

They were glad when the Old One shared his insulated container of juice. To drink from it they had to lean their heads back, squeeze, and wait for a thin stream of juice to squirt out. The trick was to keep it in the mouth and off the face. Fortunately, Durkee had brought towels to wipe up the mess. The drink kept everyone occupied and focused attention away from the heat.

The Harts were caught off guard when Durkee pulled up in front of a group of furkid houses. This new surrounding was an island of activity in a sea of emptiness. It was the last thing they expected to find in the middle of the Mises desert.

The Harts followed their guides into a fenced corral. Although they had seen many different things on Mises, the animals in the corral were the strangest. The beasts looked like a mixed-up jigsaw puzzle of several recognizable animals, perhaps somewhat like two-legged camels or furry ostriches with large lips. They were big and hairy with two thick-thighed legs, and atop the body was a hump with short wings. On top of a large neck sat a head like a llama's. They looked down on the Harts and literally dwarfed the furkids.

Just then several furkids came out to greet the newcomers. They wore long, flowing white robes with hoods that contained two little holes for their antennae. The furkids talked to the Old One and Durkee as the Harts approached the animals to get a closer look. The camp was located at the base of some huge mountain-like sand dunes which formed a picturesque backdrop. Durkee turned to the family.

"Out there," he pointed to the sea of dunes, "hovercraft do not work. Sand gets in the engines and skimmers cannot cross steep hills. They need flat land. On the other side of the dunes, we make a food from very hard milk."

"We call it cheese," Mr. Hart told Durkee.

"Long ago the only way to trade our fruit for their cheese was to cross the desert. Some still do. This place is named Maranatha after the first trader to cross."

As Durkee told the family about the ancient furkid caravans, Elizabeth and John thought they saw something appear and disappear in the desert.

"Did you see that?" Elizabeth asked.

"I sure did," John assured her.

They pointed toward the sand dunes and everyone turned to watch. At that moment it occurred again. Although heat waves made it difficult to see clearly, everyone kept looking.

"This is what the Old One brought you to see," Durkee said with a smile. The wavering movement turned into a line of objects. As they squinted, they were able to identify a large caravan.

"It looks as if it's coming here," John said.

"That's right," Durkee confirmed.

The robed furkids filled a trough with water and scurried about getting ready for its arrival. As the column of ostrich-camels came over the last row of dunes, they counted nearly three dozen animals. Led by four riders, the rest of the animals were loaded with large boxes.

"They must be very strong," Elizabeth marveled.

"Yes, they are," Durkee nodded his head. "After a few days they will be loaded with bottles of our best juice for their trip back. They travel almost twenty days with one day of rest here. This is the only watering place between our village and the other side of the desert."

The animals sensed the waiting water and began racing toward the troughs in the corral. As the Old One walked to greet the caravan, one rider jumped off her running beast and ran to embrace him.

"Are they old friends?" Mrs. Hart asked.

"Yes, she is his sister."

"Did we come to meet his sister?" Mrs. Hart wondered.

"Oh no," Durkee stated. "We will be going now."

The Old One and his sister talked for a while, and then she brought some cheese and several bottles of juice to the hovercraft.

"Let's go," Durkee said, and before they had a chance to think, they were skimming back to Durkee's village, eating cheese and drinking juice.

There was one more thing the Old One wanted to do. Somewhat bewildered about the purpose of the first trip, the hot and tired Harts wanted a cool shower more than another adventure. But finally the skimmer came to a stop where some furkids were building a three-legged house. It was similar to the ones the Harts had already seen.

"Is this what we're supposed to see?" Mr. Hart asked impatiently.

"Not all of it," Durkee smiled. "Ah, here he comes now."

Durkee pointed to a furkid child who carried a sack on his back. As he approached the construction workers they all turned to greet him. The youngster opened his sack and traded something with every worker. The Harts couldn't see what was being traded but Durkee called him over to buy some. The Old One took the child's coconut-like fruit, tore off the stem, and tipped it up to drink its contents.

"Many children grow these plants, cool them in streams, and bring them to places where others are working to sell them," Durkee explained.

"Kind of like an ice-cream truck on Earth," John said as he tore off the stem of his plant and took a big mouthful of the cool liquid inside. He shuddered and quickly spit it out.

"Yuukkk! It's awful! I need some water!"

Durkee and the Old One were surprised but amused. The rest of the family sniffed at John's open fruit and handed their own to Durkee. He shrugged, a gesture he had learned from the Harts.

"This is all very interesting, but what does it have to do with our spaceship?" Mrs. Hart asked.

Durkee spoke to the Old One, then translated: "He says there is an important lesson to be learned from these two experiences."

Mr. Hart was noticeably upset. He wasn't sure the whole day hadn't been wasted. "What we've seen today seems a bit nonsensical to me. Watching your global actions," he continued sarcastically, "is globaloney."

"Maybe so," Durkee tried to assure him, "but there is some sense here. The Old One says the answer to fixing the Apollo is in this riddle."

"More riddles? It's as if we ask for the time and you explain how to build a clock. What does cheese and bitter juice have to do with anything we need to know in order to get home?" Mr. Hart screeched.

Elizabeth said, "Come on, Dad, give Durkee a

break. They brought us out here for a reason, so let's see if we can figure this out. They were all doing something, right?"

"Yes," Durkee's voice implied she was on the right track.

Elizabeth went on, "And they were doing those things because they saw a need?"

"Then they got an idea?" John added.

Mr. Hart scratched his bearded chin as he shook his head. "So?" He sounded frustrated.

"Oh, I think I see what you're getting at," Mrs. Hart contributed. "The furkids were working to help themselves by providing things for others. They all were looking for market opportunities."

"Yes, you saw the furkids using their ideas to meet needs," Durkee said.

"On Earth we call them entrepreneurs," Mrs. Hart said. "Those who put ideas to work to do what otherwise wouldn't be done."

The Old One smiled as the conversation turned in the direction he had hoped.

He talked and Durkee translated: "New things come from entrepreneurs. Better things begin with the ideas of the individuals who make them work. Without this effort, ideas aren't worth much."

Mr. Hart suddenly snapped his fingers. "Eureka! The Old One is trying to tell us that the best way to get something done is to do it ourselves." He was beaming. "All right, kids, we're going into the marble-making business!"

The Old One and the Harts began to laugh and joke about making marbles. The day hadn't been wasted after all. Necessity is still the mother of invention. If you need marbles and can't find them, learn to make them, or find some other way to solve your problem. Meanwhile, Durkee was concentrating intently on snapping his furry little fingers.

During dinner the Old One discussed his idea for manufacturing marbles. Mr. and Mrs. Hart and Durkee listened and asked questions. The family's biggest concern was time. Could it be done in only a few weeks? Regular marbles, like those that can be bought in any toy store on Earth, would not work in the ship's gyroscope. They would have had to meet stringent requirements and would need very complicated machinery.

Mr. Hart was encouraged by the Old One's help. He seemed to know everyone. After an hour on the phone, the Old One announced he had found someone willing to sell them a machine that made metal ball bearings and an engineer who could help convert the machine to work with glass. The family was excited, but also realistic. Could they earn enough money? Would there be enough time? Although the children went to bed with more hope than ever, their parents worked late into the night, planning what had to be done.

When the children awoke the next morning, their parents were sitting in the same places, still discussing the task ahead. John and Elizabeth dressed quickly to make sure they didn't miss anything.

"Where are we going today?" John asked.

"We have to borrow money to set up our business," his mother told him. "Thankfully, Durkee's parents will let us use the thuralemm factory. But we have to buy the machine, hire the engineer, and purchase the material needed to start making marbles."

"But who would loan us money?" John asked. "We don't even live here, and as soon as we get the marbles, we'll be leaving."

Mr. Hart explained, "Durkee's parents will actually borrow the money."

"My goodness," Elizabeth said, "won't it take a lot of money? And what if no one buys our marbles?"

"Well," Mrs. Hart tried to explain, "if we sell lots of marbles, then Durkee's folks will make money, too."

John interjected, "What if we lose our marbles trying to make marbles, Mom?"

"Funny, John, very funny," his mother chided. "As I was saying, if we don't sell enough marbles to keep the business going and produce the marbles we need for the ship, we'll have the rest of our lives to pay back the loan."

Elizabeth just said, "Oh." John looked away.

Someone knocked on the front door and Durkee's father answered. The visitor was a soft violet color and held several pieces of long rolled-up paper. Her robe had large sleeves and many pockets to hold her calculating equipment.

"This is Nancy," Durkee told the Harts. "She is one of our best engineers." After they all had a chance to shake her hand, they headed for the hovercraft. Soon, all nine were crowded into the six-seated skimmer. The children thought they would be left behind, but before anything was said, they were on their way to get a loan. They stopped first at the same bank the family had visited with Durkee. While the children waited, the others went inside. When they returned, John and Elizabeth knew it had not gone well.

"Did you get the money?" John asked anyway.

". . . No . . ." his mother answered with some hesitation. "These bankers thought the risk was too great to loan us money. None of them had ever heard of playing a game with little glass balls, and they didn't think we could make enough money to pay them back."

John and Elizabeth's silence showed their disappointment. Elizabeth reached over to take John's hand.

"Don't worry, kids," Mrs. Hart went on. "There are many other banks with money to loan. Maybe we can convince the next one that the risk is worth it. After all, everything we do is risky. Why, we even take a chance by getting out of bed in the morning."

"I know what you mean," John said sadly. "I'm beginning to wish I'd stayed in bed today."

"I don't understand," Elizabeth complained. "Why don't they just give us the money?"

"They're only being cautious," Mr. Hart told her. "Do you know what would happen if lenders gave their money to people with bad ideas? It's okay to be careful, because nobody likes to lose money."

"Otherwise, I suppose a lot of things would be made that nobody wants," John ventured.

"And those of us with good ideas wouldn't get the money to make the things everyone does want. After all, there's only so much money to loan out," Mr. Hart added.

"But the furkids will love marbles. It's a great game,"

Elizabeth protested.

"That's exactly what we're trying to convince these bankers," Mrs. Hart assured her. "We'll just try some-place else."

So off they went, admittedly a little less enthusi-astic, but not ready to give up. The Old One and Durkee's parents knew many furkids who loaned money, and they visited one after another, but with no success. By late afternoon they were really worried. Everyone was quiet as they traveled from one bank to the next. Elizabeth felt a lump growing in her throat. She wanted to cry. John wondered why he had been so eager to go on this trip in the first place.

Mrs. Hart cleared her own throat in an attempt to sound cheerful. "We'll try one more place today. Then we'll go home and do something fun tonight."

Mr. Hart rubbed his chin.

Elizabeth found it hard to believe there was any-one left to ask about loaning money. It seemed they had talked to all of them already. They pulled up at a small building with a large coin on its front, much like the other banks they had visited. The group went in-side while the children waited. They waited and watched. It seemed to take forever. John turned to Elizabeth. He didn't have to say what they both were thinking.

Suddenly a blue streak burst out the bank's door. It was Durkee at full run! He stopped at the hover craft, put both hands on the side of the door and did a full flip over the craft, landing on his feet on the other side. The children were flabbergasted!

Before they had time to ask what had happened,

Durkee shouted, "They'll take the risk! They'll take the risk! They're going to loan us the money!"

Elizabeth and John thought Durkee had taken a pretty big risk by somersaulting over the skimmer, but they were too full of delight and excitement to say it. Elizabeth bounced up and down in her seat, and as John ran to greet his parents, Durkee began to sing:

Everything we do is risky,
Every path we have to cross.
To get somewhere, we have to risk it.
To make a profit, risk a loss!

Chapter Twelve

EARTH PRACTICES AND TAXES

That evening the whole group celebrated the productive day with a huge feast. There were mountains of food and many different kinds of juices. Despite the party, Mr. and Mrs. Hart and their engineer were bent over a table, sketching designs and making changes in the mechanics of the marble machine. The guests stayed well into the evening, so the children didn't get to bed until very late. When they awoke everyone was hard at work again. Elizabeth and John were thankful that individuals from two such different cultures could cooperate and get along so well.

The all-out effort to produce and sell marbles was really intended to help the Harts return home. Everyone was busy and everyone had a job to do. Durkee's mother was talking on the telephone. When she hung up, she told Durkee to inform everyone the machine would be delivered to the thuralemm factory that very morning.

Elizabeth squealed with excitement. John punched his left palm with his right fist.

"Hot dog!" he said with relish. "We're on our way!"

"It's a start, anyway," Mrs. Hart corrected. "We have

work to do ourselves. Your father and Nancy are going to set up and convert the machine today. We hope it will be ready when we get back."

"What do you mean, when we get back?" Elizabeth quizzed.

"Someone has to go to the coast to pick up the materials we need to make the marbles."

"The coast?" the children repeated in unison.

"Great! Can we go surfing?" John asked.

"Now, John, have you already forgotten what Durkee said about cost?" his mother inquired. "Taking the time to go surfing would be pretty costly, don't you think, dear?"

"I guess you're right, Mom," John answered.

Durkee smiled and ended their confusion. "Crafts that ride on the water bring things from all parts of Mises to the coast. We are going to meet—"

"a ship!" John interrupted.

"—a ship and pick up the glass. We have already arranged to buy the material. All we have to do is go get it."

The young people were excited about going with Durkee and their mother. They exchanged good-byes with the others and were off. Once outside, John and Elizabeth were surprised to find they would be taking a hovertruck. The step to the passenger compartment was so high they had to climb a ladder. Its trailer was just like those of the trucks on Earth. Durkee started the engines with the doors open, and it sounded much like a jet engine at takeoff. Once closed, the doors sealed out most of the noise and vibration. Easing the craft out of the parking lot, Durkee slowly wound through the village.

As they came to an unfamiliar section of town, they were surprised to see a freeway system. The hovertrucks and skimmers on the road were moving faster than Durkee had ever driven on the grass paths. This highway appeared to be made of ceramic tile or some kind of plastic.

As Durkee turned onto the main road, John asked, "Are we actually going out there? They're really hauling."

"You want to see hauling? Watch me put pedal to the metal!" Durkee exclaimed in his 1950s cool talk. The kids laughed.

"You've been watching too many Earth movies," John kidded.

"But my driving is safe," Durkee reassured every-one. "I have traveled these roads many times."

Soon they were moving at the incredible speed of 150 miles per hour, and Durkee flipped on some music to help everyone relax. It was an exciting way to see Mises. As they drove through treeless plains and tow-ering mountains they were awed by the beauty. Oc-casionally they passed buildings Durkee identified as toll houses. Their travel was being recorded so a bill for highway use could be sent to them later. They noticed the traffic was gradually getting heavier and guessed correctly that they were nearing a large city.

Mrs. Hart was pointing out a particularly strange looking hovercraft when Durkee turned off the high-way and pointed his blue finger to their right.

"Watch over there," he commented.

As the family looked, the hovertruck passed the

last hill and they caught sight of the ocean.

"It's beautiful," Mrs. Hart gasped.

"Hey, Mom," John shouted, "surfs up! Just like Hawaii."

"It's wonderful," Elizabeth commented, "but its still different from our ocean."

Waves were crashing on the white sandy beaches. High above the ocean level, they could look far out to sea. Birds were circling all around and gigantic ships could be seen in the distance. On this day dozens of sailboats were in the harbor. Their colorful sails were absolutely beautiful.

Durkee pulled off the road so they could watch the boats heel in the wind. Each gust provided a thrilling spectacle, and the violet-tinged sky made the sight even more magnificent. Mesmerized, they hated to leave, but there was a job to be done.

Down the road a few turns and fifteen minutes later, they entered the port city. They could see Durkee must have made this trip before. He easily wound his way to the docks through what seemed a maze of back streets along the curving waterfront. He went straight to the dock where several ships were unloading cargo.

Weathered furkids operated cranes that moved huge crates to waiting hovercraft. Durkee moved the truck closer to the wharf and sent John and Elizabeth with a slip of paper to the supervisor on one of the ships. As the furkid in charge took the paper he stared at the kids in disbelief. He, too, was different looking. As a matter of fact, all those working around the dock had brighter shades of fur, were shorter, and had longer antennae than any of the furkids John and Elizabeth had seen.

"All those furkids look different," John commented when they had returned to the hovertruck.

"Yes," Durkee answered, "they are different in looks, and we do not speak the same language. Is that the way it is on Earth?"

"Yes," Mrs. Hart acknowledged. "There are many different kinds of people and languages on our planet. There is something else different about this whole port, though, and I can't seem to figure it out."

"I know what you mean," Elizabeth said. I've watched ships load and unload in Honolulu, but this is not the same."

The three Hawaiians watched the furkids at work to see if they could discover the difference.

Suddenly Mrs. Hart said, "There's no port authority, no custom's agents, no inspectors or other uniformed people."

"Are those strange animals?" queried Durkee.

"Oh no." She and the young people laughed. "On Earth, they are the people who make sure that goods going in and out of our country pay import and export taxes."

"What are taxes?" Durkee rubbed an antenna.

"That is the money they are required to pay the government," she tried to explain.

"Why?" Durkee asked.

"Well . . ." Mrs. Hart thought for a moment. "For several reasons. One is to make sure foreign goods are not cheaper than the same goods made in our country. Another is so our government can get money from foreign traders instead of from our own people."

Durkee puzzled over this explanation for a moment and then began to laugh. He held his little belly and laughed until tears came from his eyes and wet the fur on his face. The Harts were bewildered.

"I must not understand," he finally managed. "I thought you said your government was trying to make things more expensive!" And he chuckled again.

"That *is* what I said," Mrs. Hart assured him.

At that, Durkee stopped laughing and stared with wide-eyed disbelief. "Why?"

"To protect the people who make the same type of product, so they continue to make it," she told him.

"But . . . but," Durkee stammered, "why would anyone buy something they could buy cheaper somewhere else? Why would your government make everyone spend more money?"

"To make sure we all have jobs," she concluded.

"But . . . doesn't foreign trade mean you trade things? Doesn't trade create jobs?"

Mrs. Hart hadn't thought of that. "I'm not really sure, Durkee."

"Why don't you just let everyone buy things as cheap as they can get them? Doesn't that make more sense?" Durkee seemed very confused about Earth practices.

"It sounds like a good idea to me," John agreed. "If you made only what people wanted to trade, everyone would be better off."

"You might be right," Mrs. Hart admitted. "I never thought about it before. However, it is a good way for the government to raise money without making people pay."

"What?" Durkee asked. "How could you raise the cost without causing that business to raise its price? If you raise the cost with a tax, then the company has to raise its price in order to pay the tax. It's really the buyers, not the sellers, who pay the taxes."

"He's gotcha there, Mom," John kidded.

Just then a resounding thump on the bed of the hover truck indicated that the first of three boxes of glass-making material had been loaded. The other two quickly followed and the group was ready to head home.

"I'll need to think about what you said, Durkee," Mrs. Hart told him.

"Not me," John said. "It already makes sense."

Durkee and the Harts arrived at the factory just after the ball-bearing machine had been completely converted to handle glass. Thanks to the engineer they had hired, the machine was ready to be tested. Mr. Hart climbed into the truck as soon as it stopped and opened one of the containers. Scooping out a bucketful of crushed-glass sand, he poured it into the part of the machine that housed the melting pot. The glass bits sparkled like a million little jewels. Within a few minutes the glass was melted and the computer readouts began to appear.

"Let's see if this thing works," Mr. Hart said nervously.

Durkee's father pushed a blue button on the side of the machine, and a small glob of red-hot glass oozed into a slowly spinning metal bowl. The turning bowl forced the cooling glass into a round shape. As the red glow faded, the ball was abruptly shuttled to rotating tubes and S-shaped grooves. With each cycle the glass ball became rounder and harder until it finally looked like a perfect marble.

At the other end of the machine Mr. Hart and Nancy had set up a series of devices to test the finished product.

"Watch carefully, kids," he instructed. "This is very important."

He placed the marble on the first testing device, a scale. "Too heavy," he said. In response, Nancy made a slight adjustment on the machine.

A second test indicated the marble was not perfectly round, and yet a third indicated it was not magnetically neutral.

"As you can see, this is going to be a long, slow process. We think . . . we hope we can get one marble per day that is acceptable for use as a bearing in our stabilization unit. But every single marble will have to be checked. We need at least twelve, and we have only fourteen days to get them."

The children looked at each other. They were a bit discouraged by their father's phrase "hope we get one marble per day," but they tried not to show it. The silence in the room ended with the thunk of another marble. Elizabeth ran to help put it through the tests. But hope as she might, it turned out to be even more defective than the first.

Mrs. Hart put her arm around Elizabeth. "Don't worry. Sometimes failure is the key to success. We'll get the hang of it. If we were on Earth we probably would be just getting the permission we would need from the government to even start this business. So you see, things really are going quite well." As if to reinforce her comment, the machine produced another marble. "Why don't you and John wait here until there are enough marbles to teach the Old One how to play? If he likes it, he could become our best advertisement. Thank goodness the newspapers like to talk about us, because that will help, too. We hope to sell enough marbles in the next week to buy more materials."

The machine was adjusted to full speed so the marbles would come out faster. John grabbed two handfuls of rejected ones and motioned the Old One to come outside. In the parking lot behind the factory, he drew a circle in the dirt with a stick and divided up the marbles. He dropped all his marbles into the center of the ring and told the Old One to do the same. Giving one marble to the furkid, John gripped another tightly between his thumb and index finger and shot it into the ring. Amazingly, one marble was knocked out of the ring, and John made a show of putting it in his pocket. He shot again, missed on purpose, and nodded to the Old One that it was his turn. The furkid knelt down and tried to arrange his fingers like John's. He made a good effort, but his marble barely dribbled into the ring. He looked a little embarrassed. But John motioned him to keep trying, and finally he shot the marble with a little speed, but no accuracy. One shot had missed the ring entirely, and John had to run to retrieve it.

"Thank goodness," Elizabeth said. "I was beginning to think furkids couldn't shoot marbles with only four fingers."

The Old One indicated it was John's turn to shoot, and he got down on his hands and knees to watch. His eyes were only inches from John's hand. When John missed, the Old One gripped his marble, sighted down his hand like a gun barrel, and took a deep breath. His whole arm tensed as the marble flew forward. It hit in the very center of the circle; marbles flew everywhere, and two were knocked out of the ring. The Old One jumped and laughed with joy as he put them in his cloak. Then he insisted on playing the game again and again. When John became tired, Elizabeth took over.

The children were saved when their father came out and handed the Old One a big bag full of marbles. Knowing he had more important things to do, the Old One quickly departed.

In the meantime, Durkee was asking Mr. Hart about hiring more furkids. They had heard about the new business and were anxious to help out.

"How many should I hire?" he asked.

"Seven will be enough. It's terrific that they came to us. I was just thinking about the process involved in hiring more workers."

"Hmmmmm," John puzzled. "I thought everything was running smoothly on Mises, and now I discover there are furkids without jobs. Things aren't so perfect after all."

"Perfect?" Durkee asked in amazement. "You thought things were perfect?"

"Well," John said, "if everyone doesn't have a job,

there must be something wrong."

"Perfect," Durkee said the word again. "Life is change, not perfection. Some of those who want to work are looking for their first job. Others have just moved here, and some have worked for koereadums, or businesses, that no longer exist."

"See," John said, "that's what I mean. Some companies have gone out of business. There must be something wrong."

"Is change wrong?" Durkee asked.

"What do you mean, Durkee?" Elizabeth asked.

"I will show you." And he led them into his parents' office. On one wall was a picture of a furkid mounted on a large animal. The animal looked part horse and part bird. Its legs and head were similar to those of a horse, but the wings sprouting from its body and folded alongside its round midsection were like an eagle's. The saddle between the wings looked much like the ones the children had seen on the animals in the desert.

"In the old days," Durkee explained, "this is the animal most of us rode. Many worked at making the seats that tied on the animals, and many grew the food that fed them. Then someone invented skimmers and vehicles with wheels. Most of the people who worked on the old things had to find new jobs. But the improvement in transportation made more business possible and many new jobs available. Before all that happened, though, some were without work."

The children were once again deep in thought over this new insight.

But Mr. Hart had no time to waste in meditation.

He told Durkee, "Hire two to help here with the machine, two to help the Old One get the marbles to the stores, and three others to help us unload the Apollo. We'll need to unload every unnecessary thing from the ship if we want to take off without a booster rocket."

Chapter Thirteen

THE MARKET PLACE

The race to meet the strange comet had everyone working overtime. They knew what had to be done and were determined to do it. The machine continued to turn out marbles, one after another. With six days of glass material left, the Harts listened to Durkee's sales report. Their only hope, it seemed, was to get the game out on the market and sell enough to buy another load of glass. This had to be done by the seventh day.

John and Elizabeth spent most of their time putting the finished marbles through the tests to see if they met the standards of the guidance system. At noon on the first full day, Elizabeth found their first usable marble. She had carefully put it through each test, and when it passed the first two she grew excited. Then she put the little sphere through the last test to measure its magnetic and conductive properties. As the meter stabilized she realized the marble was perfect.

"We've got one!" she yelled, and the whole factory came to an excited standstill.

Unfortunately, the next two days passed without a

single acceptable marble. Marble production, however, was growing by leaps and bounds. With twelve in each clear plastic bag, the marbles were packed sixty-four bags to a box and distributed by the Old One. But sales were not going well. Distribution and marketing took longer than anyone had expected. With just a little money trickling in, Mr. and Mrs. Hart were worried about keeping the business running.

On the fourth day of production John and Elizabeth went with their parents to help unload the Apollo. They were amazed at all the things that had been taken out. The panels and equipment that would have constructed the solar fields were stacked high enough to fill two Apollos.

Mrs. Hart helped unfasten the parts ready to be unloaded. Exercise machines, zero-gravity beds, and everything else not absolutely necessary for the ship's operation was removed. The massive storerooms were emptied, and footsteps could be heard echoing off the bare walls. Even the water tanks and the grow-lights for the hydroponic gardens were dismantled and taken out. A small quantity of food and water still in the lockers was tagged indicating it too would be unloaded. Tears came into Elizabeth's eyes when she saw a tag on the books and special things she had chosen to bring with her.

"It's really necessary," Mrs. Hart assured her with a hug.

As the ship was emptied, the young people experienced confusing emotions. Although they were glad to see the Apollo made ready for their trip home, the sight of the gutted ship made them sad. Mrs. Hart transferred the fuel from the extra tanks to the main ones. Then she pushed the series of buttons to release the cylindrical extra tanks from their mountings. When the furkids rolled the heavy tanks off the Apollo's wings, they landed with a double thud in the soft ground around the ship. Only the area directly in front of the ship was clear for the takeoff, which would take place only if the marbles sold well enough to keep the machine producing, and if the machine produced enough of the right kind of marbles, and if. . . . There was a long list of really big "ifs."

Elizabeth, John, and Mrs. Hart returned to the factory to pick up Mr. Hart for supper. Although the machine had produced another good marble, only two had been made in four days, and the ship needed ten more.

That was the best of two pieces of news he shared with them. The other was that they were not selling enough marbles. Everyone in the village had bought some, and furkids of all ages were playing the game; there was no need to buy more.

They had to start selling marbles outside the village. And time was running out.

On the fifth day the machine produced another perfect marble. Unfortunately, only two days' worth of glass material remained. Gloom set in. Durkee and the Harts knew the company would eventually make enough money, but they needed it now. The Harts were learning the hard way that some things just take time. Perhaps they had been grasping at a straw when they set up the marble koereadum, but it had been their only chance.

Breakfast on the sixth day of production was quiet. The furkids felt sorry for the humans stranded on their planet.

John played with his food but tried to be cheerful. "At least we all have jobs. It looks like the company is going to be a big success."

Elizabeth wasn't in the mood for that kind of cheering up. Her lower lip started to quiver. She dropped the knife she was using to cut her giant strawberry and ran outside. Mr. Hart started to follow her, but his wife put a hand on his arm and shook her head. He sat down and tried to concentrate on his meal.

John took a few more bites, excused himself, and walked outside to look for his sister. She was sitting beside the stream that ran behind Durkee's house. He stuck his hands in his pockets and walked slowly toward her.

"I'm sorry, Elizabeth." He looked at the ground. "I just thought that if we have to stay here, we might as well make the best of it. I know just how you feel."

"All my friends are in Hawaii," she said, "and I miss them so much. I'd just like to be home. Mises will never be home . . . it'll never be home."

"I know," John admitted.

"It's just not fair," her voice raised in complaint. "If everything works so well here, why can't we get the money we need to keep making marbles? The only money we had was from tours of the Apollo, and almost all of that went to pay for the dragon medicine."

"You're right," John agreed. "Dad said that in another week or so, when the business is doing better, we could get another loan." John was aware he was not making his sister feel much better, but he continued anyway "The only way to make more money is to sell marbles all over Mises, but that will take more trucks and drivers and bookkeepers and factory workers. By the time that happens, the comet will be long gone."

Elizabeth was throwing little rocks into the stream. "Why can't we get away from here? Everything works so well for everybody else. Why not for us?"

"You know," John said, "the problem is—"

"Money," Elizabeth filled in the blank, "We need money! Either we steal it—and that's not an option—or we earn it."

"What could we do to earn money?" Elizabeth was becoming more interested. "It's a little late for a hovercraft wash or selling cookies door to door."

"That wouldn't raise enough, anyway. We need lots of money." John held his arms out as far as he could reach.

"Well, I brought a guitar and some other things I could sell," Elizabeth said thoughtfully. "But I'm sure that wouldn't be enough. I saw them yesterday beside the rest of the stuff that was—" she stopped suddenly and looked at her brother.

And together they completed her thought: "Taken off the . . ." And they both yelled, "Apollo!"

Elizabeth was off the ground and running way before John could move. They rushed to Durkee's door and burst through together. The room still seemed filled with gloom. Nancy, the Old One, Durkee, his parents, and their own parents looked up surprised by the sudden entrance as the two stood panting.

Both started to speak at once: "We can—" and each stopped to let the other talk. Finally, they both turned to the confused group and, in perfect unison, cried out, "We can sell the stuff from the Apollo!"

Mr. and Mrs. Hart said nothing for a minute, trying to figure out what they had just heard. Then a flash of inspiration crossed Mr. Hart's face. He stood up and slammed his fist on the table. Durkee's parents and the rest of the furkids jumped. Durkee translated, and instantly, a spontaneous celebration erupted. Elizabeth and Durkee clasped hands and danced around the room. The Old One howled with laughter, and Mrs. Hart kissed John.

"Why didn't we think of that?" Mr. Hart asked. "It's so simple!" He slapped the palm of his hand against his forehead. The Old One saw this and laughed even harder. He understood exactly what it meant. The other furkids laughed and soon they were all slapping their foreheads.

When the laughter began to die down, Mrs. Hart said, "Durkee, we need the Old One to get on the phone. We're going to sell everything we unloaded. And while you're at it, order us another load of glass sand. If we leave now, we can be back with it tonight. Okay?"

"Okay!" yelled the blue translator.

All their despair had vanished. The marble koereadum was back in business.

In the following days the old thuralemm factory saw more activity than ever. Trucks arrived and left three and four times a day. The things on the Apollo brought enough money to do everything necessary to expand the business.

As the fame of their product spread and their deadline grew closer, more and more reporters showed up at the factory. The Old One stopped his advertising campaign, since newspapers and magazines had articles about the Harts in every edition.

Each day was exciting. Even the marble machine did better than expected. On the twelfth day there were fifteen usable marbles, three more than they needed.

Mr. and Mrs. Hart spent the whole day putting the spherical-silicate-antimagnetic-semiconductive gyroscopic stabilization-unit bearings into their proper place and testing out the entire mechanism. They ran checks all afternoon, attempting to estimate the new weight of the Apollo and the way it would handle in flight. After many computer-simulated take-offs, they returned to Durkee's home.

The next day turned out to be the most enjoyable the Harts had spent on Mises. Stopping production for the day, they gave the workers time off with pay. The group of friends went sightseeing to a zoo and a museum. Late in the afternoon they visited a sporting event, played by two teams of eight on a large round field with a ball so big it occasionally rolled right over an unfortunate player. Mrs. Hart thought surely they were trying to break the huge ball.

After supper they all went to the Apollo to check it out one last time. Scheduling their lift-off for noon the next day, Mr. and Mrs. Hart checked every instrument in the ship and ran the computer through its final tests.

"Shall we start the engines?" Mrs. Hart asked.

"Now's as good a time as any," he answered. "Besides, our furkid friends might enjoy it."

John was sent outside to warn the reporters not to stand behind the rocket engines while they were being tested. Mr. and Mrs. Hart were seated at the control panel, checking the list of procedures necessary for the test firing.

Everyone was excited. Mrs. Hart checked the last item on the list.

"Commence low thrust engine test," she said, and Mr. Hart pushed a big red button.

The silence was terrible.

"Try again, honey," Mrs. Hart said, trying to sound calm.

Mr. Hart tried again, several times. The children felt as if the universe had collapsed around them. The pleasant day they had spent together was shattered.

Mr. Hart continued to click the button on and off. Then he turned to the bank of meters. He looked at one in particular and tapped it several times with his pencil. The red arrow that had been stuck far to the right suddenly flipped to the far left. Staring at the meter, he leaned back in the chair with his hands behind his neck.

Without turning, he said, "We've had a liquid oxygen leak. The alarm failed to tell us it had evaporated."

Mrs. Hart leaned over her panel with her head in her hands. The children were dead silent.

"Come home," Durkee said. "We can think about it in the morning."

"You don't understand, Durkee," he was told. "We are helpless without liquid oxygen. Our fuel won't burn. We have no more money and no more time."

"We tried, Durkee," Mrs. Hart told him. "Why don't you thank all our friends for their help? I think we'll just spend the night here. We still have blankets, and these acceleration chairs are pretty comfortable. We'll see you in the morning. We need to spend the night here, alone together."

Durkee's antennae were not the only pair quivering. They all had known something was wrong when the engine failed to start. As the last furkid quietly left the ramp, John and Elizabeth started to cry. Without a word, their parents sat on the cabin floor beside them. When their tears finally stopped, Mrs. Hart gathered blankets to make their chairs more comfortable. As the family held hands, and prayed like never before, John and Elizabeth finally fell asleep. Mr. and Mrs. Hart stared in disbelief at the big window that disclosed the alien sky they would live under for the rest of their lives.

Although the night of sleep was only temporary medicine for the homesick family, it was abruptly interrupted early in the morning by the sound of music. Mr. Hart woke first. As he went to the door, the rest of the family jumped up.

Through the open door of the craft came a flood of carnival sounds. Acrobats, musicians, jugglers, and at least a thousand furkids were gathered around the Apollo, and starbirds were everywhere. Tents of beautiful colors had been pitched, and the whole crowd was laughing, enjoying the spectacle and the beautiful sunlit day.

"Why are they laughing?" Elizabeth asked. "How can they be so happy that we failed?"

"Oh no," Mrs. Hart assured her, "they're just trying to make us feel better. The news of the liquid oxygen leak must have spread fast. It's amazing so many came."

"I'll bet they don't even know we can't take off," John said glumly. "They probably came to watch us leave."

A starbird that had been floating around the outside of the Apollo came down in front of the open hatch. It stopped at eye level and stared, and suddenly it was gone, flashing away into the crowd.

A familiar furkid came walking toward the ramp. The Harts saw that Durkee was carrying a bag over his shoulder. He walked up the ramp but stopped short of the door.

"We have brought you a gift," he announced as if

nothing at all were wrong.

"Thank you, Durkee," Mrs. Hart said.

"Oh! This is not the gift," he said as he handed her the bag. "Inside are the things the people gave you at the Old One's cave. We didn't want you to forget them."

The Harts noticed the whole crowd had become silent, as if everyone were listening to the conversation through Durkee.

"There is your gift." He pointed at the tents below them. The family watched as two hover trucks pulled out of one of the tents.

"What are we going to do with trucks?" John sounded as if such presents were a dumb idea.

Durkee was silent, and Mr. and Mrs. Hart saw what the children did not—the massive tanks on the trucks.

Mrs. Hart grabbed her husband's arm. "Those are tank trucks, aren't they?"

Mr. Hart was absolutely amazed. "Durkee," he asked, "do you know what liquid oxygen is?"

"Yes," Durkee laughed, "and so does everybody here." He swept his arm around to indicate the whole crowd. "And we have brought you some as a going away present."

The Harts were so happy they hardly noticed the cheering of the crowd. But for Mr. and Mrs. Hart, the celebration was short-lived. They needed to go to work.

Mr. Hart went inside to prepare the ship for receiving the precious fluid. John and Elizabeth were stunned but smiling. They ran down the ramp to greet Durkee's parents, Nancy, and the Old One.

"We can never thank you enough," John cried.

Actually, the two young Harts said much more than that, but the furkids understood only how grateful they were and smiled back. A furkid selling food brought them some chocolate-covered bananas. Durkee came down and joined them.

"Why, Durkee? Why did you wait until now?" Elizabeth asked. "Why didn't you help us when we thought we couldn't buy any more glass sand?"

"Didn't you want to do it yourself?" Durkee asked. She shrugged unsurely, and he continued. "You were doing wonderfully. Why should we ruin the fun of doing something for yourself? I suppose we could just have given you the money to make your parts, but it was your adventure, not ours. Just because we do not force anyone to help those who need it does not mean we don't care." He laughed. "We just like to have a choice. It is really more fun to help someone when you don't have to!"

John and Elizabeth were a little embarrassed at admitting their feelings about Mises. John gathered the courage to ask his usual question, "Then is no one really in charge here?"

"Of course there is," Durkee laughed.

John was shocked, but the blue furkid went on, "we all are in charge of our own lives. Our society is the result of each person seeking to improve his or her life. We don't need leaders for that. Come now and walk through the crowd with me. Everyone here put their money together to buy you liquid oxygen. Would you like to meet some of them?"

When the loading was complete and everything had checked out, Mr. and Mrs. Hart joined their children and walked around through the crowd of friends. They smiled at everyone and everyone smiled at them. For several hours the family thanked and hugged those who had helped them so much. They were very grateful.

"You know, Durkee," Elizabeth told him, "you're right! Giving is more fun when you don't have to do it. And it's more fun to receive a gift that way, too. We'll always remember you. Thank you for helping me understand things I've never thought of before."

When the sun shone almost directly overhead, it signaled the time for takeoff. Everyone said good-bye through Durkee, and there were lots of smiles and hugs and tears. As the family disappeared inside, Durkee cleared the crowd away from the Apollo.

Inside the ship the family was nearing the end of their checklist again. The red button worked this time, and the powerful rocket motors roared. The crowd watched the Apollo edge forward until suddenly the rockets exploded and the Apollo hurtled into space.

The Harts immediately started looking for their comet. The ship maneuvered perfectly as the computer picked up the comet, coming back from its trip around the sun.

As they raced to meet the glowing ball, their unspoken fear was that this might not work. It was possible that they would go through the comet and be headed back toward Mises. What if they collided with the comet? It was all very scary.

As the comet grew closer, the Apollo swung around to meet it. The glowing mass grew and grew as they raced toward its center.

"Buckle in, kids."

"We're buckled."

"Hold on!"

"I am."

"Me too."

The ball of super-fireworks was coming faster and faster. Suddenly the two objects met in the pure silence of space.

"Thank you, God."

"No kidding."

As the comet raced on in the opposite direction, all eyes were frozen to the window; a planet seemed to hang there, suspended in space.

"Now that's home," Mr. Hart sighed as he flicked on the radio.

"I see Hawaii," John exclaimed.

"It looks wonderful," Mrs. Hart said with tears in her eyes.

Elizabeth closed her eyes and said a silent "Thank you, dear Lord" for Durkee and the rest of their friends who had made their return to Earth possible and taught them so much about life.

As the comet moved swiftly into the darkest depths of space, Mr. and Mrs. Hart turned the Apollo around so they could watch it disappear. The children stared with wonder at the comet that had taken them to a new world of creatures, life, and economic freedom. They all felt it had given them a new attitude about their blue and green world circling below, and some new ideas that Earth just might like to try.

SYNOPSIS OF ECONOMIC PRINCIPLES

ACTION: The attempt of people to relieve dissatisfaction or achieve something. Examples of beneficial student actions would include: If you drop something, pick it up. If you open a door, close it. If you make a promise, keep it. Whatever you borrow, pay back. Begin early to play the thank-you game. And do nothing to a fellow student that you wouldn't want done to yourself.

This book is about choice (action) and its consequence.

BANKS. Banks safekeep other people's money. Because of their substantial funds on hand, they loan much of it in return for interest.
"I thought banks just protect money," John said. "Oh, banks do more than that," Mrs. Hart explained. p. 56

BARTER: Trading one thing for another without using money. Societies would probably stay underdeveloped if they continued to barter.
"Without money, people would spend most of their time arranging trades instead of making the things other people want." p. 48

BUYER: One who buys things in the marketplace for a price.

"It looks as if they're selling their fruit to whoever will pay the most money."

"Can you think of a better way to decide who should get what?" p. 46

CHOICE: Exchanging one thing for another. Choice is really an action that has costs, benefits, and consequences. All of life is about choice.

"We just like to have a choice. It is really more fun to help someone when you don't have to!" p. 138

COMPETITION: When many sellers have the same thing for sale in the marketplace. It encourages sellers to supply the highest quality things for the lowest price. A system of social cooperation by which everyone strives to improve their position.

"Is cooperation the same thing as competition?" Elizabeth asked.

"In a way, yes," Durkee affirmed. "[People] compete to be the ones who cooperate best." p. 74

CONSUMER SOVEREIGNTY: The idea that the consumer is king. The power of the consumer to determine through their "dollar votes" what is produced.

"It looks as if they're selling their fruit to whoever will pay the most money," John observed. p. 46

CONTRACT: A legal agreement that binds persons together in an agreement.
"[Contracts] are a way of dealing with the things that are yours." p. 87

ECONOMIC PROBLEM: The conflict arising because people's wishes are limitless and the things in the world are limited.
"Will you ever reach a point where you won't want anything else?"
"No." said John. "I suppose not!"
"That's right," his father agreed. "Most people want more than they have." p. 10

ECONOMICS: The study of human actions, how people produce, distribute and consume goods. *Apollo* is about economics.

ENTREPRENEUR: An idea person; a decision-maker. One who undertakes a project and reaps the rewards or the losses of his/her idea. One who takes risk by investing money in a business venture where there is no guarantee of profit.
"Yes, you saw the furkids using their ideas to meet others needs," Durkee said.
"Those who put ideas to work to do what otherwise wouldn't be done." p. 109

EXCHANGE: Trading things.
"This [exchange] probably takes place because it results in everyone being better off." p. 29

FREEDOM: Liberty from slavery or oppression. Private ownership is *the* prerequisite for freedom.
"Come to think of it, you have the freedom to choose because you are free to own."
"That's right," said Durkee. "They take care of the surissaluh because they own them. Everyone benefits because of private property." p. 86

GOVERNMENT INTERVENTION: An act on the part of government which interferes with the market process.
"I must not understand," he finally managed. "I thought you said your government was trying to make things more expensive!" And he chuckled again. p. 120
(Government laws usually interfere with markets and voluntary exchange.)

INFLATION: Whenever the money supply is increased faster than productivity, prices go up. It is a period of rising prices.
"When a government prints a batch of money, but the economy doesn't produce more goods, the price of everything goes up." p. 102

INTEREST: Income received for lending money. The price a borrower pays for borrowing money.
"Well, instead of storing dried fish to feed his family, the fisherman could have borrowed fish from his neighbor while he was making his net. Now, don't you think the fisherman who loaned him the fish should be repaid, plus some? That extra he

would be paid is called interest." p. 56

INVESTMENT: New capital resources that generate more income and jobs. The process of directing savings into specific enterprises.
"Well, without investment we wouldn't have nearly as many of the nice things in life. All our houses, churches, cars, clothes, and books were produced because people were willing to save, invest and work." p. 57

MACHINES: Mechanical devices that get a job done.
"Isn't a tool something you use to make things a whole lot easier? With this little machine (the nut-cracker) Durkee managed to fix us lunch in a few seconds." p. 40

MARKET: A situation where buyers and sellers can communicate and agree upon prices and exchange products and services.
"Whenever someone buys, sells, or trades something, it's called a market." p. 45

MONEY: Anything which acts as a medium of exchange, store of value, or standard of value. Coins and checks, for example, can be exchanged for a good or service, but they also can be held as wealth for a later use. Anything used to facilitate trade.
"Money has value only when everyone agrees it has value. For a society to work, everyone has to believe money can buy things."

"Money is just a way to keep our wealth in small packages." p. 50

NEED: Something required. Things needed to sustain life, like food, clothing, shelter, and medical attention.
To John, wants and needs were always the same. (see want) *p. 4*

OWNERSHIP: Legal right to the possession of a thing.
"Anything you own is yours to treat in any way you want, as long as it doesn't interfere with someone else's private property."
"[Y]ou have the freedom to choose because you are free to own." p. 86

POVERTY: Lack of something necessary or desirable. Poverty is a subjective concept. In the U.S. it is defined as the costs for essentials for families of various sizes.
"You know someone is poor when they don't have all the things they want, and you feel sorry for them." The Old One asked, "Do you have everything you want?"
"No, John answered, "but I'm not poor." p. 95

PRICE: The value of something expressed in money.
"They charge the right price. So everybody gets the amount they want."
"If the price is too low, then everyone would want to go, and there aren't enough seats for everyone.

Besides, if they didn't charge enough, they couldn't pay the orchestra what they want, and then no one would play. You see, without prices, how could you decide who should get things?" p. 67

PRIVATE PROPERTY: The legal right in a market economy for people to buy, own, and sell economic things.

"You are free to choose because you are free to own. p. 86

"You must remember that you are your most important property. On Mises, our law says you can do anything except disturb another's private property or contracts." p. 88

PROFIT: The amount of money that is left from sales after a business pays all its costs. The gain from an action.

"What do you call selling something for more money than it costs to produce it?"

Mr. Hart answered, "We call that making a profit."

"[P]rofit and loss tell everyone how much of everything to produce." p. 70

RISK: The possibility of a loss. The chance one takes of losing money on a business venture.

"Why don't they just give us the money?" Elizabeth asked.

"They're only being cautious," Mr. Hart told her. "It's okay to be careful, because nobody likes to lose money." p. 112

SAVINGS: The putting away of wealth for use at a later time.

"In order to build a tool or machine of any kind, you have to save things instead of using them. Hawaiians in the old days had to fish almost all the time just to have enough to eat. But by storing dried fish, they were able to use the time to make new nets to catch even more fish." p. 40, 41

SCARCITY: Whenever there isn't enough of something to satisfy everyone. Unfortunately, there is seldom, if ever, enough of what everybody wants. *"Most people want more than they have. Whenever there is not enough of something, we say it is scarce." p. 10, 11*

SELF-INTEREST: People are encouraged to pursue their own interests, decide on an occupation and try to gain a satisfactory level of rewards. This is the motivating influence in a market economy. *"In a way, everyone is a little business. We sell our work and ideas, just as businesses sell goods and services." p. 61*

SELLER: One who offers goods or services in the market place.

"The furkids were working to help themselves by providing things for others. They were all looking for market opportunities." p. 109

SPECIALIZATION: Whenever someone becomes very good at a particular job. Although specialization makes us become more dependent on each other, it also helps us produce more of the things we want.

"On Earth we call it specialization when everyone does what each one does best. That way, we all have more of the best products to choose from." p. 59

TARIFF: A tax levied by government on imports. A tariff has the effect of increasing the selling price of the good, and therefore is very expensive to all consumers. Tariffs make things more expensive and destroy international trade.

"I must not understand," Durkee said. "I thought you said government was trying to make things more expensive!" p. 120.

TAXES: Money paid to local, state and federal government by citizens and businesses to support government workers and their ideas. A charge levied by a government authority upon persons or property for public purposes.

"If you raise the cost with a tax, then the company has to raise its price in order to pay the tax. It's really the buyers, not the sellers, who pay the taxes." p. 121

TOOL: Something useful for attaining a goal. A train. A hammer. A computer, ideas, knowledge, and information are also tools. Their most important function is to increase production.

"Isn't a tool something you use to make things a whole lot easier?" p. 40

TRADE: Giving up something to gain something. Everybody is better off. It is a product of cooperation. *"No one forces them to buy or sell. Those who buy would rather have the fruit than the money and those who sell would rather have the money than the fruit. It works out just right. Everyone's happy."* *p. 46*

VALUE: The worth of anything to a specific person or persons. Value is subjective. That is, it depends on the person doing the valuing. The exchange value of any loaf of bread, or painting, or day's work is whatever others will offer in exchange.
"But marbles aren't that valuable," Elizabeth was puzzled.
"If you were dying of thirst on a desert, which would be more valuable-an expensive diamond or a drink of water?" said her mother. p. 23

WANTS: Desire for things. Needs are necessary. Wants are desires that never stop.
"To John, wants and needs were always the same." *p. 4*